No. C305227
Author CARTER
Title Aladdin

CW00411617

AVON C
PLEASE RETURN BC

19.NOV82 58076
12.MAY84 40236
-6.SEP84 21562
-2.MAY85 62111
28.NOV85 56131
14.JUN86 19671
20.AUG87 57713
-4.SEP87 08412
-3.NOV87 30830

10. AUG 88
08. APR 89
21. OCT 89
05. NOV 90
17. FEB
10. MAY 94
07. JAN 97
14. MAY 93
15. SEP
10. MAY 06
13. APR 05

CL 100

WOODSPRING CENTRAL LIBRARY 34 - 35
Boulevard Weston - s - Mare BS23 1PL
Monday - Friday 9.30a.m. - 8.00p.m.
Saturday 9.30a.m. - 5.00p.m.
Tel. Weston - super - Mare 24133

NEW

Copyright 1935 by Samuel French Ltd

This play is fully protected under the copyright laws of the British Commonwealth of Nations, the United States of America, and all countries of the Berne and Universal Copyright Conventions.

All rights reserved.

It is an infringement of the copyright to give any public performance or reading of this play either in its entirety or in the form of excerpts without the prior consent of the copyright owners. No part of this publication may be transmitted, stored in a retrieval system, or reproduced in any form or by any means, electronic, mechanical, photocopying, manuscript, typescript, recording, or otherwise, without the prior permission of the copyright owners.

Samuel French Ltd, 26 Southampton Street, Strand, London WC2, or their authorized agents, issue licences to amateurs to give performances of this play on payment of a fee. **The fee must be paid, and the licence obtained, before a performance is given.**

Licences are issued subject to the understanding that it shall be made clear in all advertising matter that the audience will witness an amateur performance; and that the names of the authors of plays shall be included on all announcements and on all programmes.

The royalty fee indicated below is subject to contract and subject to variation at the sole discretion of Samuel French Ltd.

Basic fee for each and every performance by amateurs in the British Isles — Code C

In territories overseas the fee quoted above may not apply. Application must be made to our local authorized agents, or if there is no such agent, to Samuel French Ltd, London.

ISBN 0 573 06402 4

PRINTED IN GREAT BRITAIN BY

BUTLER & TANNER LTD, FROME AND LONDON

ALADDIN

As produced, December 1933, by the Children's Theatre Company under the management of Miss Joan Luxton, at the Embassy Theatre, London, N.W.3.

CHARACTERS

(In the order of their appearance)

Character		Actor
LONKA	Imperial Attendants (tall)	*Nicholas Phipps.*
CHORTA	Imperial Attendants (short)	*J. Forbes Williams.*
GRAND VIZIER		*Basil Radford.*
	(By kind permission of Arthur Gibbons.)	
PEKOE (his son)		*John Gatrell.*
PRINCESS BADROULBADOUR		*Ann Casson.*
SING LOH-HI	(Maids-in-Waiting to the Princess)	*Elfrida B[illegible]rgiss.*
SING HI	(Maids-in-Waiting to the Princess)	*Esmé Herschell.*
SING TUH	(Maids-in-Waiting to the Princess)	*Myra Owen.*
ORACULASHTA (the Oracle)		*Maud Jolliffe.*
ABANAZAR (a Magician)		*Brember Wills.*
1ST GOLD SLAVE	(Abanazar s servants)	*Peter Ashmore.*
2ND GOLD SLAVE	(Abanazar s servants)	*Alan Gordon-Brown.*
GOMISH (Slave of the Ring)		*Norman Shelley.*
ALHIRA (Slave of the Lamp)		*Joan Luxton.*
WIDOW TWANKEY		*Charles Hickman.*
ALADDIN		*Geoffrey Wincott.*
1ST BOY		*Ronald Hickman.*
2ND BOY		*Peter Ashmore.*
3RD BOY		*Royalton Straker.*
SHOPKEEPER		*Alan Gordon-Brown.*
HIS WIFE		*Verah Patterson.*
A CUSTOMER		*Ann Cotton.*
JASMINE (a Mule)		*Ronald Hickman.* *Royalton Straker.*
THE EMPEROR		*Norman Shelley.*
FATIMA		*Maud Jolliffe.*

Carpet Boys, Citizens, etc.

The Pantomime produced by GEOFFREY WINCOTT.

NOTE

If the size of the cast presents a difficulty, the parts of boys, maids-in-waiting, slaves, can be either doubled or combined as one character, or in some cases omitted, as the producer arranges.

SYNOPSIS OF SCENERY

ACT I

SCENE 1.—The Market Place in Peking.

SCENE 2.—Cave of the Gold Makers.

SCENE 3.—The Market Place Again.

SCENE 4.—Widow Twankey's Laundry.

SCENE 5.—Entrance to the Ruby Cave.

SCENE 6.—Inside the Ruby Cave.

ACT II

SCENE 1.—A Corner of the Street, Peking.

SCENE 2.—Widow Twankey's Laundry.

SCENE 3.—The Street Again.

SCENE 4.—The Garden of Aladdin's Palace.

SCENE 5.—The Palace in the Desert.

SCENE 6.—The Street in Peking.

SCENE 7.—Aladdin's Palace in Peking.

NOTES ON SCENERY, ETC.

When the directions R., L., C., are given, they stand for right, left, and centre of the stage, when used by the actors.

P. is Prompt, or L. side of the stage.

O.P. is Opposite Prompt, or R. side of the stage.

The stage should if possible be arranged with curtains that can be drawn across, half-way down stage from P. to O.P. sides.

For music used in this Pantomime, see list at end of book.

The dresses are those of the traditional Arabian Nights period.

Alhira, impersonating the flame of the lamp, should be dressed in colours of yellow and flame, and her head-dress flame-shaped.

Widow Twankey should be comic, and her skirt could be wired with crinoline wire for the garden scene.

The scenes are arranged with alternating front scenes, in order to enable the full sets to be changed without long waits.

The scenery should be quite simple, different places being indicated by one or two outstanding pieces of furniture. For instance, stalls in the market scene, laundry equipment in the widow's house, and a rich divan in the desert scene, etc., etc.

The inside of the Ruby Cave is the most difficult to suggest. In circumstances where scenery is not available, packing-cases and boxes can be stacked to look rock-like and covered with crimson cloth. The " jewels " can be dressed in robes of reversible material, one side dull for the rocks, and the others bright and jewelled, so that when the dancers turn round the effect is one of brilliance.

In the Palace Garden, flowers and shrubs can be arranged, so that they can be removed quickly. After the lamp is exchanged, the stage should be left quite empty. A suggestion is to have a fence or balustrade with one side flowering, and the other painted to represent dust and sand, and this could be turned round in the darkness.

ALADDIN

ACT I

SCENE 1

Market Place in Peking.

This SCENE *is a full set, if possible stalls on either side of the stage, and seat or well* C. *At the rise of the* CURTAIN, *market folk, boys, etc., discovered playing cards, selling goods, strolling about.*

CHORUS. Make way, her royal highness is bathing to-day,
She's coming this way! She's coming this way!
Make way! Please observe how we're shouting make way!
Down on your knees, all good people.
Make way! Just observe how we're shouting make way!
Shouting, make way! Shouting, make way!
The beautiful *Bad*roulbadour bathes to-day—
Shut up your peepers, good people!

(LONKA *and* CHORTA, *two litter-bearers, detach themselves from the rest of the crowd and sing:*)

Chop chop, ching ching, litter-bearers we,
Summoned to the palace, velly instantly,
Run away at oncey, velly suddenly,
LONKA (*introducing himself*). Lonka—
CHORTA (*doing the same*). Chorta—
LONKA }
CHORTA } (*together*). Litter-bearers we.

CHORUS. Ching ching,
Chop chop,
Down upon your knee,
For we know that heads off—
Choppy chop can be.

LONKA. Lonka,

CHORTA. Chorta.

LONKA / CHORTA (*together*). Go as quick can be——

(*They exit up* R.)

CHORUS. Me shutty eyes up,
Me no see!

(*At the finish of the chorus they all prostrate themselves on the ground, eyes tightly shut. The* GRAND VIZIER *enters from up* R., *and at the same time* PEKOE *enters from* L. *They pause and greet each other with great formality.*)

GRAND VIZIER. Pekoe! It is. My son, blessing upon your honourable head. (*He holds out his arms.*)

PEKOE. August and venerable parent, I tender you my duty.

GRAND VIZIER. Come to my arms.

(PEKOE *crosses to him.*)

PEKOE. I kiss your feet.

(*They incline their heads towards each other in Chinese fashion, without touching, and then they drop all formality of manner and come down stage together. The* GRAND VIZIER *repeatedly trips over the recumbent figures of the townsfolk.*)

(*Fretfully.*) Father, why have you summoned me back from my holiday in such mad haste?

GRAND VIZIER. Hist! (*He trips.*)

PEKOE. Father, do look where you are going. What are they all doing that for? (*He points to the kneeling people.*)

GRAND VIZIER. Hist! The Princess Badroulbadour

goes to the bath-house to-day. Have you forgotten all your court etiquette ? All good citizens must prostrate themselves in the presence of royalty when it—I mean they—them—those, well, when whoever it is goes bathing. (*Speaking to the crowd.*) You can get up, the Princess will not be here for a little while.

(*The crowd obeys slowly.*)

Don't hang around, can't you see I'm busy ? Don't encumber me . . . Be off !

(*The crowd stand aside in groups.*)

PEKOE. What is it, father ? Need we waste any more time ?

GRAND VIZIER. Not so fast, boy, not so fast. You forget that your holiday has lasted three years, and in three years a great deal can happen. For one thing, our Princess is three years older.

PEKOE (*with impatience*). Of course, father.

GRAND VIZIER. She is now of marriageable age. (*He taps* PEKOE *with his finger.*) Marriageable—do you get me ?

PEKOE. No, father.

GRAND VIZIER. The pursuit of pleasure has not brightened your wits, my son. Give heed, and borrow a glimmer from mine. The Princess shall marry you.

PEKOE. But I'm not sure that I want to get married, father.

GRAND VIZIER. Pshaw ! I shall call a conference, and the conference will advise the Emperor to abdicate——

PEKOE. Oh, if it means being Emperor, I shan't mind so much. Let's get on with it. Where is the Princess ? (*He moves towards the exit* L.)

GRAND VIZIER. Not so fast, not so fast. It's not as easy as all that. The Princess has a violent temper.

PEKOE. I'll soon teach her to control that.

GRAND VIZIER. Three years ago she *lost* it.

PEKOE. That's all right, then ; she hasn't got it.

GRAND VIZIER. She flew into a rage so terrible that

all the court quaked in their shoes. Then the Princess sulked for a whole year, refusing to speak—now it is believed that she cannot.

PEKOE. Cannot?

GRAND VIZIER (*shaking his head impressively*). For two years our beloved Princess has not spoken one word.

PEKOE. How does she make her wants known?

GRAND VIZIER. She throws things at her maidens if they do not move fast enough . . . shoes, or something heavier if there's anything handy. The Emperor has consulted magicians of every sort. They all say the same thing. Only one who loves and is loved will have the power to unseal her lips. Now you see why I sent for you.

PEKOE. Why, father?

GRAND VIZIER. Brighten up, my boy, brighten up. You can love, can't you?

PEKOE. I've never thought about it.

GRAND VIZIER. Well, then, think now. What good are you if you can't do a little thing like that?

PEKOE. That's all very well——

GRAND VIZIER. Don't argue. Get busy at once. *Love*, I tell you. You love me, don't you? (*No answer.*) Don't you?

PEKOE. No . . . yes . . . I mean—of course I do . . . that is . . .

GRAND VIZIER. Very well, then, if you love me you can love anybody. (*His son protests.*) Set about it. I don't want to hear any objections—you do as you are told, and leave all the details to me.

(*A gong is heard off stage* L.)

Stand aside! The Princess is coming.

(*They stand at one side of the stage. The* CHORUS *sing as before.* "Make way," *etc.*)

The music changes, and the three maids-in-waiting enter down L., *followed by* LONKA *and* CHORTA, *carrying the* PRINCESS *in a closed litter. They set it down* R., *and immediately squat by the litter-poles and fall asleep. The maidens group themselves at the side.*

(*Sung by the maidens as they enter:*)

One, two, three,
Maidens we.
Every day,
Making our way.
SING LOH-HI. I can sing high,
SING HI. and I sing low,
SING TUH. and I sing too,
ALL THREE. As on we go—
One, two, three,
Maidens we.
Every day
Making our way.

(*At finish of trio, the* PRINCESS *draws aside the curtains of the litter and looks round slowly. She gives a rather malicious little smile at the prostrate forms of the crowd.*)

GRAND VIZIER (*pushing* PEKOE *forward*). Go on, speak to her. What are you waiting for? Now mind, love her. Do as I tell you.

PEKOE (*nervously*). Princess, er . . . beautiful Princess . . . er . . . er . . .

(*The* PRINCESS *turns at the sound of his voice and gives him a cold, haughty stare. He stammers, and the* GRAND VIZIER *nudges him.*)

Er . . . er . . . What is it, father? What do you mean?

GRAND VIZIER (*pushing* PEKOE *on one side*). Princess, I want you to meet my son . . . he is er—— (*Aside to* PEKOE, *who is plucking at his sleeve.*) Idiot! (*To the* PRINCESS.) No, no, I don't mean that. . . . Although I, his father, say it, he is worthy to touch the hand of the great and glorious mistress of a thousand peoples. . . . (*He becomes aware of the cold stare with which the* PRINCESS *is regarding him, and also begins to stammer.*) . . . er . . . peep . . . er . . . peep . . .

(*The* PRINCESS *closes the curtains with a click. The* GRAND VIZIER *tries to explain his weakness.*)

Nasty little tickle in my throat . . . speaking in the open air . . . She's taken to you, my boy. I knew she would. Emperor, my lad! A throne! That's what's coming to you, my boy, a throne—that's what's coming . . .

(*A shoe is flung out of the litter and hits* PEKOE.)

PEKOE (*ruefully*). That is what I've got, father. (*He holds up the shoe.*)

(*The* PRINCESS *is heard to laugh. She claps her hands, and* LONKA *and* CHORTA *wake instantly and lift the litter. The maidens gather round, and the* PRINCESS *exits* R. *to same music as at entrance. Just as they reach the exit,* SING LOH-HI, *who is watching* PEKOE *with sympathy, runs back with a pot of salve in her hand.*)

SING LOH-HI. Try this. I always use it for my bruises. See, like that. (*She touches his cheek, puts the pot into his hands and runs after the others.*)

PEKOE (*looking after her*). Like that? (*He repeats her action.*) Her fingers were so soft, like a dove's feathers. Father, did you see her?

GRAND VIZIER. See who? Pah! A serving-wench—a slave. Come on, don't waste time, we've made a very good beginning.

PEKOE (*with dismay*). Beginning? You don't want me to go any further, do you?

GRAND VIZIER. Certainly.

PEKOE. But did you see her face? The Princess hates me.

GRAND VIZIER. Any emotion does in a love affair. Think what it would mean to be Emperor. The finest steeds in the royal stables; the richest jewels in the city; the rarest foods, wines, slaves——

PEKOE. Slave? (*Looking out where* SING LOH-HI

has gone.) Could I have any slaves I liked to wait upon me?

GRAND VIZIER. Of course, of course, have courage boy, have courage. (*He turns to go and trips over one of the citizens.*) Get up, for Heaven's sake, get up; it's all over for to-day. Do you know, you are a positive danger to the community, spreading yourself all over the place like that?

1ST CITIZEN. Me solly, great highness, velly solly, but if me caught looking at Princess, my head, it come off. That velly dangerous——

GRAND VIZIER. Only to yourself, my boy, only a danger to yourself. *Now* you are a danger to everybody. (*To* PEKOE.) Come along, a valuable animal has been stolen from the royal stables. I have to go and see about offering a reward to the finder . . . Come along.

(*They go towards the opening up* L. *The crowd jump up and sing.*)

CHORUS. Come on once again, we can work and play,
Work and play, all the day,
Come on, the Princess has now gone on her way,
Get up from your knees, all good people.

(*They push and scramble.*)

Look out where you're going, get out of the way,
Get out of my way, get out of my way,
Look where you're going, get out of the way,
Hush up your noise, you rude people.

(*During the singing of this last chorus* WIDOW TWANKEY *enters down* L., *pushing a small hand-cart full of linen piled inside. She calls*:)

WIDOW. Aladdin, Aladdin! Where is that boy? Has anyone seen Aladdin . . .?

(*As she walks across the stage, calling, the* CURTAINS *close, and there is a Black Out of the lights, or the* CURTAIN *falls for a few minutes in order to set the next scene, which is a front one.*)

Scene 2

The Cave of the Gold Makers.

During the change of scene the music gets softer and softer, and the Widow's *call of* " Aladdin " *is taken up by* Oraculashta, *so that when the lights go up* Oraculashta *is discovered seated on cushions at* r. *of the stage, dealing out cards on the ground in front of her. She is reading the cards, and murmurs to herself.*

On the opposite side of the stage two slaves are tapping at a piece of gold.

The Curtains *at the back must be divided in the* c. *so that* Alhira *can use them as an entrance.*

Oraculashta (*dealing out the cards*). Aladdin . . . Aladdin . . . diamonds for wealth . . . hearts for happiness. Happiness, courage, love, all waiting for the fearless one. . . . (*Her voice dies away, but she goes on reading the cards to herself.*)

1st Slave. I am so tired of hammering gold. Gold, gold! What use is it all? (*He hammers violently, and a piece of gold flies across the stage.*)

2nd Slave. Take care! Take care! Abanazar is coming.

(Abanazar *is heard off stage, muttering to himself, and spluttering in a rage.*)

He sounds as if he is in a terrible rage!

1st Slave. Oh! (*He dashes to pick up the gold.*)

(Abanazar *enters* l. *The slaves cower back.*)

Abanazar. Careless, careless! Don't treat the beautiful metal too harshly or it will turn on you and crush you; crush out your miserable, idle, cunning lives. It is your fault, I suppose, that I find my storehouse so full that I cannot get into it to count how much gold I have hidden away.

1st Slave. What are we to do, Master?

ABANAZAR. What use is it, if I cannot touch it, my beautiful gold ?

2ND SLAVE. There is nowhere to put it, Master.

ABANAZAR. The cave by the seashore.

1ST SLAVE. It is full, great one.

ABANAZAR. The seaweed cave, where the shrimps live ?

2ND SLAVE. All full, O greatest !

ABANAZAR. You lie. There is still one cave unfilled . . . the ruby cave. (*The slaves fall on their faces.*) Aha, there is room there. (*He rubs his hands, chuckling.*) To-day you shall take the gold and store it in the ruby cave . . . the ruby cave.

(*The lights go up and down again suddenly, there is a crash and* GOMISH, *a dwarf, appears.*)

I wish you would not do that. If you must appear so suddenly, do it more quietly.

GOMISH. Master summoned me ?

ABANAZAR. I did not . . . (*He looks at his hands.*) Oh, I must have rubbed my magic ring by mistake. Very well, now that you are here, take all this gold and pack it away.

GOMISH. Where, master ? All the caves are full.

ABANAZAR. Have you forgotten the ruby cave ? There is yet room and to spare in the cave of the crimson jewels.

(GOMISH *falls down in terror.*)

What is it now ?

GOMISH. Master, you know no one can enter the ruby cave who has fear in his heart. Have you forgotten the lamp ?

(ABANAZAR *starts, as if in fear himself.*)

ABANAZAR. Pah ! Cowards all !

(*He then drives the slaves off. They exit* R. *and* L.)

Am I always to be maddened, baffled ? Fetch me Alhira. Where is my ring ? (*He finds the ring on his finger and rubs it violently.*) Alhira, at once. . . .

(GOMISH *does not move.*) Well, why don't you do as I tell you?

GOMISH. Master, you know that Alhira is a greater slave than I am. I cannot do it without more magic.

ABANAZAR. Magic! Ah, of course, more magic. Now, let me see . . . (*He takes a wand from his belt and waves it in a large circle, draws figures on the ground, muttering to himself.*) Cum hoome, cum zoome, cum fleeter zoomer . . . Aga, maga, zest and roomer. . . Alhira appear, appear . . .

(*During this incantation* ALHIRA *appears very calmly and softly just behind* ABANAZAR, *who continues to invoke her, louder and louder, until he suddenly turns round and finds her watching him.*)

(*In exactly the same tone that he used to* GOMISH *on his entrance.*) Oh, there you are, are you? I wish you would not do that; if you must appear so suddenly, make more noise about it.

ALHIRA. You are so silly, Abanazar, you don't need all that fuss. (*She sits down near* ORACULASHTA.)

ABANAZAR. Get up at once; treat me with proper respect.

ALHIRA. If you want a slave, you've got one there already.

(GOMISH *snarls at her.*)

You want my advice, don't you?

ABANAZAR. Nothing of the kind.

ALHIRA (*getting up*). Oh, very well, then; I wish you hadn't disturbed me.

ABANAZAR. Now, now, wait a minute, don't be so hasty. It is my gold, what am I to do with it? I have no joy in making it any more.

ALHIRA. Of course not. You have too much already. What is the use of gold if you never use it? You must do something with it.

ABANAZAR. But what?

ORACULASHTA (*turning up a card*). Diamonds, wealth . . . fortune!

ABANAZAR. What was that?

ALHIRA. Oraculashta. Why not consult her?

ABANAZAR. Consult her? Well, I might . . . (*He draws away.*) But suppose she says something I don't like? (ALHIRA *takes his hand and pulls him towards* ORACULASHTA.) Now be careful, don't be in such a hurry . . .

ALHIRA (*standing with him in front of* ORACULASHTA). Oh, Oraculashta, greatest of all wise ones, listen to us, I pray you, and help us.

ORACULASHTA (*without looking at them*). What is your trouble?

(ALHIRA *pushes* ABANAZAR *forward.*)

ABANAZAR. I am a goldmaker. All my days I have made gold, but now there is so much of it that there is nowhere to put it.

ORACULASHTA. What is the good of keeping gold? You must let it loose.

ABANAZAR. But where?

ORACULASHTA (*reading the cards*). On earth the people groan and stint themselves. I see poverty, want and hunger. Take your wealth down to earth, Abanazar. Use it, before it crumbles in ruin at your feet.

ABANAZAR. But how?

ORACULASHTA (*again consulting the cards*). Red . . . for flame! Have you forgotten the lamp? For years the magic lamp of plenty has lain unused. Find it, take it down to earth and use it.

ALHIRA. The lamp! Oh, could I but serve it once again!

ABANAZAR (*shrinking away*). The lamp! I am afraid of the lamp.

ORACULASHTA. Only a youth, a mortal without fear can enter the ruby cave and fetch the lamp.

ABANAZAR. Where can we find such a one?

ORACULASHTA. Use your wits, Abanazar. Go down to earth and search. Only the fearless ones can win the treasures of the earth. . . . (*She continues to deal out the cards.*) Hearts for happiness . . . diamonds for wealth . . . fortune . . . love . . .

ABANAZAR (*speaking at the moment* ORACULASHTA *begins to read the cards*). The treasures of the earth! Riches, fame and power!

ORACULASHTA. Take care, Abanazar, take care. If you go down to earth with only greed in your heart, and forget the power of Love . . . beware the fearless youth, beware, beware . . . (*her voice grows fainter and fainter*) beware Aladdin . . . Aladdin . . . (*She falls asleep.*)

ABANAZAR. Aladdin . . . Aladdin . . . where can I find this Aladdin?

ALHIRA (*who has been watching* ORACULASHTA). Master, she is asleep.

ABANAZAR (*very annoyed*). Tch! Tch! When will she awaken?

ALHIRA. No one can say, no one ever knows. But, master, she has said enough. Go down to earth and search out this fearless lad. I long to serve the lamp again. (*Eagerly.*) O master, do go.

ABANAZAR. I don't say I won't, but I mustn't be hurried. How could I make the journey, do you think? Could I float down, on a cloud? (*He makes a step indicating a floating motion.*)

ALHIRA (*shaking her head*). Too startling. You had better go more like an ordinary mortal, so that they won't suspect you.

ABANAZAR. Do you suggest that I just go, without any ceremony at all, wandering about Peking, shouting, "Has anyone seen a boy without fear?" Ridiculous!

ALHIRA. You will be guided. When Oraculashta puts an idea into our heads, she helps us with her thoughts. Our business is to get started. O master, do start.

ABANAZAR. That is all very well, but I ought to have a proper means of transport. If I mayn't fly I am certainly not going to walk.

GOMISH (*who has crept up close and been listening*). Master, I know the very thing. This morning we led astray the Grand Vizier's favourite mule. If you rode him back to Peking, he would know the way.

ALHIRA (*clapping her hands*). Seek out the stolen mule and bring him hither.

(*Exit* GOMISH.)

Now, master, away, waste no more time. I shall await the summons of my lamp with all impatience.

ABANAZAR (*fretfully*). You are not going to leave me? I can't go all that way alone.

ALHIRA. The slave of the lamp can only become visible to mortal eye in answer to the call of the lamp. Go, master, go quickly, find the fearless youth; go, find Aladdin!

(*The lights go out, and the* CURTAINS *are closed quickly.* ORACULASHTA *murmurs* "Aladdin," *and* ABANAZAR *mutters it, so that their voices mingle with that of* WIDOW TWANKEY, *who begins to call again as the* CURTAIN *rises on the Market Place. The others cease as soon as the change of scene is made.*)

SCENE 3

The Market Place.

Opening chorus the same as in Act I, Scene 1. *At the end of the chorus all exit except three boys, who push and tease* WIDOW TWANKEY, *who is by this time in the* C. *of the stage with small push-cart.*

WIDOW. This laundry gets heavier and heavier every time I fetch it. I don't know what they are wearing up at the Palace, but it feels like lead to-day. Now, boys, have any of you seen my Aladdin? Come along, speak up now; have you seen Aladdin?

BOYS (*shouting together*). No.

WIDOW (*is at first stunned by the noise, then recovers herself*). Pardon? (*As she sees they are going to shout again, she puts her fingers to her ears.*)

Boys (*as before*). No.

Widow. I gather that the answer is in the negative. Am I right? (*Boys prepare to shout again.*) No, don't tell me, let me guess. Now, look here, I am going up that hill to fetch a few undies from the villa yonder. I shall leave the cart here for a moment. Now I trust you, mind. I shall expect to find it here when I return, just where I left it . . . Hands off . . . Fair's fair . . . Honi soit qui . . .

(*She trips and exits.*)

1st Boy. What a lark! What shall we do with her cart?

2nd Boy. Let's tip the clothes out.

3rd Boy. Let's take them to the river.

1st Boy. Come on, then! (*He takes hold of the handle.*) Oh, it is heavy!

2nd Boy. Tip the whole lot out, and chuck the cart into the river.

Aladdin (*poking his head out of the clothes*). Not while I'm in it.

Boys. Aladdin! It's Aladdin!

Aladdin. Stop shouting my name all over the market place. Don't you realize it's washing day at our laundry? I never see the fun of working if I can play.

(Song—*optional.*)

(*They squat on the ground, playing cards.*)

Tell me, has the Princess come back yet?

1st Boy. No.

Aladdin. Is she as beautiful as they say?

2nd Boy. How can we know? No commoner dare look upon the Princess.

1st Boy. She must be wonderful.

3rd Boy. I think she must be stupid; she never speaks.

2nd Boy. The Emperor has offered great rewards to the one who can make the Princess speak.

1st Boy. Yes, he's going to give him the Princess in marriage.

ALADDIN. I would rather find the Grand Vizier's mule. The reward for that is great too.

1ST BOY. Mules are not as dangerous as women.

ALADDIN. I wasn't thinking about danger.

1ST BOY. Don't be too boastful.

ALADDIN. That's not boasting. If I am not afraid of animals, why should I be afraid of women?

3RD BOY. A woman who's a princess can have your head chopped off.

(*Music heard off stage.* "One, two, three, *etc.*," *sung by trio of maidens.*)

Look out, she's coming!

1ST BOY. I'm off. I'm tired of lying on my face. Come on.

2ND BOY. Come on, Aladdin, I shan't stay.

3RD BOY. Nor me.

ALADDIN. I'm going to look, I've always meant to look one day. Ever since I saw the Princess entering the temple one feast of lanterns. I shall stay.

1ST BOY. You wouldn't dare!

ALADDIN. If I thought I could see her face, I'd dare anything.

1ST BOY. Well, keep your head down, idiot!

(*The three boys run off.*)

(*The music swells louder, and the* PRINCESS *enters as before. The* MAIDENS *sit at one side,* LONKA *and* CHORTA *fall asleep at once. The* PRINCESS *draws the curtains and looks round at the empty market place without seeing* ALADDIN.)

ALADDIN (*half to himself*). You are beautiful, as beautiful as they said. (*Falling on one knee.*) O Princess, why have you decreed that none may look upon your face? (*The* PRINCESS *hears him and slowly turns towards him.*) Beauty such as yours would give joy to the whole world.

(*The* PRINCESS *prepares to hurl her shoe at him.*)

You may kill me if you like, I'm not afraid, I don't care now that I have looked upon your face.

(*The* PRINCESS *claps her hands, and with a gesture makes a sign to the maidens to look the other way. They immediately sit in a row with their backs to the* PRINCESS *and* ALADDIN.)

PRINCESS. Come here.

(ALADDIN *goes towards her slowly.*)

Come nearer. Who are you?

(*Directly the* PRINCESS *speaks, the three maids click their fans and put their heads together. The* PRINCESS *pulls* ALADDIN *down to sit by her side on the litter.*)

Why did I speak, do you think?

ALADDIN. I don't know, Princess.

PRINCESS. But who are you? What is your name? Why won't you tell it to me?

ALADDIN. Do not ask me, Princess. I am the poorest lad in all your kingdom and you are the greatest lady. It is enough if I have helped to give the beauty of your voice to the world again.

PRINCESS. My voice is beautiful, isn't it? I am glad I have spoken again. I think I shall enjoy listening to my own voice.

ALADDIN. Most women do, Princess.

PRINCESS. Then think how they will enjoy listening to mine, which you say is more beautiful than any.

ALADDIN. That is not quite the same thing, Princess.

PRINCESS. You have a nice voice too; it is not unpleasant to me at all.

(*Duet.*)

ALADDIN. Princess, your abode is a palace of gold,
While I am the humblest your kingdom does hold.

PRINCESS. Princesses in palaces captive can be,
And though you are humble, 'twas you set me free.

ALADDIN. Your voice is like silver of bells in the air.
PRINCESS. But 'tis not of silver the humble should care.
ALADDIN. Oh, had I the wealth of the Indies at choice,
I would cast it away for the gold of your voice.

(*At the end of each verse the maidens put their heads close together and repeat the refrain as if whispering behind their fans.*)

(*At the end of the duet there is a crash of a gong off stage.* LONKA *and* CHORTA *jump to their feet.*)

CHORTA. The royal gong, your most radiant highness——

LONKA. The royal coffee will be served——

CHORTA. His most merciful majesty the Emperor——

LONKA. Will show no mercy at all to your miserable slaves——

CHORTA. If the most beautiful princess in all the world——

LONKA. Is late for the royal elevener.

(*The sentences are spoken very quickly one after the other.*)

PRINCESS. Coffee sounds good.

(LONKA *and* CHORTA *give little squeaks and run off.*)

Do you see, strange boy, they will spread the news that I have spoken? Do you like coffee? Come, too.

ALADDIN (*drawing back*). It would not be fitting, Princess.

PRINCESS (*taking his hand*). Anything is fitting that I see fit to do. I do not wish you to leave me.

ALADDIN (*indicating his dress is in rags*). But like this?

PRINCESS. I do not care that you are in rags, (*she looks at the hand she is holding*) and not over clean. Come.

(*Another crash of the gong, and the crowd comes running on, with the* GRAND VIZIER *and* PEKOE, LONKA *and* CHORTA, *etc.*)

GRAND VIZIER. The news has reached us, Princess! Peking is ringing with the glad tidings.

(ALADDIN *hides behind one end of the litter.*)

Ere long you will hear it ring, the bells will begin, ringing out the glad news of your betrothal.

PRINCESS. My betrothal? What do you mean?

GRAND VIZIER. Your father has promised your hand to the man who could coax you to speak, the man who could—

(ALADDIN *slips away.*)

—make you fall in love. And to think that it is my son . . . (*He is overcome with emotion and shakes his son's hand violently.*)

PEKOE. No, father.

GRAND VIZIER. What do you mean—no, father?

PEKOE. It was a stranger . . . Listen, father. (*He draws the* GRAND VIZIER *aside and whispers to him.*)

PRINCESS. Sing Loh-Hi, Sing Hi, come here. (*They approach slowly.*) Instantly, tell me, what are they talking about—what do they mean?

SING LOH-HI. I dare not tell you, Princess.

SING HI. Don't ask us, Princess.

PRINCESS. Speak, or I will have you beaten. (*They fall on their knees.*) Speak, I command you.

SING LOH-HI. 'Twas said, Princess, that you would only regain your speech if you were spoken to by one who loved you, and who—who—— (*She is overcome.*)

(*The* PRINCESS *turns to* SING HI.)

SING HI. And—and—someone with whom you yourself fell in love—— (*She is overcome.*)

(*The* PRINCESS *dismisses them with a gesture, they run back to* SING TUH.)

PRINCESS. Is this possible? To be in love, and not to know it?

GRAND VIZIER (*coming forward*). Quite, Majesty, quite. My son here . . .

PRINCESS (*cutting him short*). Where is *he*? The boy who spoke to me? Find him at once. (*She looks round.*) He was a grubby boy, in rags.

GRAND VIZIER. A commoner? Spoke to you?

PRINCESS. Have I not said so?

GRAND VIZIER. Impossible.

(*The* PRINCESS *is very angry.*)

Pardon, pardon, Princess, I mean it *ought*—to have been impossible. He couldn't have understood what he was doing.

PRINCESS (*ecstatically*). Yes, he did. I am beginning to understand what it means to be in love. Yes, take me to my royal father; he shall keep his vow. Quickly, I say, to the palace; the joy bells shall ring out.

(*She claps her hands, the procession forms. The* PRINCESS *leans out of her litter and speaks to the* GRAND VIZIER.)

If this boy is not found, and at once, your head shall pay forfeit. Your head and your son's.

(*The* PRINCESS *exits, followed by the crowd.*)

GRAND VIZIER. There you are. See what you've done—messed it all up! Well, I've got to find that boy, and what's more, get him out of the way before I find him. You had better try to help me. Go and prattle to that waiting-maid, get some clue. If you don't marry the Princess I'll spoil the little game of anyone else who tries to.

PEKOE. Be careful, father. However little value you put upon your own head, I'd rather keep mine. I'm accustomed to it.

(*Exit* PEKOE.)

GRAND VIZIER (*looking off stage*). How do I know where to look? Who's that? Yes—no, it's some stranger . . . (*Looks down the road, shading his eyes.*) Yes, no, *yes*—it is the mule that was stolen . . . my

Jasmine . . . Well, I'll spoil his little game to be going on with.

(*Enter* Abanazar, *riding face to tail of mule. There is a speaking-tube attached to the mule's ear. The* Grand Vizier *stands in their way.*)

Halt, there! You cannot pass.

(*The mule lifts a leg and kicks him; he falls under mule.*)

Abanazar (*speaking down the tube*). What is the matter, Jasmine? Why have you stopped? Eh, what? (*He listens through the tube.*) What's that? Under your legs? (*He peeps over the mule at the side and sees the* Grand Vizier.) Excuse me, sir, are you without fear? Entirely without fear?

Grand Vizier (*getting up and keeping a wary eye on the mule*). Certainly I am. (*The mule makes a movement, he skips out of reach.*) Kindly control that animal. Er . . . wouldn't it be easier if you faced the other way?

Abanazar. Sir, I am a man of some education: in my youth I studied history: I was taught to look only at the past, the better to understand the present. Now, when I set out upon my travels, I continue in the same manner. As when studying history, I perpetually look backwards, always consulting the road I have just been along, the better to be prepared for the road that lies ahead.

(Duet—*optional.*)

(Abanazar *gets off the mule and holds out his hand.*) Shake. Pleased to meet you.

Grand Vizier. Shake hands with a common stranger? Certainly not.

(*The mule threatens him, and he seizes* Abanazar's *hand in fright, and then turns his gesture into a handshake.*)

An exception, an exception to every rule. Er . . . wouldn't it be better if you tied your mule up somewhere?

ABANAZAR (*speaking to the mule*). Jasmine. (*He mutters to him.*) Habacasha-galassha—(*then loudly*) Parkah !

(*The mule parks itself, sitting at one side of the stage.*)

GRAND VIZIER. By the way, it is not your mule at all. Where did you get it ? Can you tell me that ?

ABANAZAR. I found it—it was straying.

GRAND VIZIER. You dare to tell me—that tale . . . (*He splutters with rage.*)

ABANAZAR. Now, now, now, nothing is ever gained by fretting. You appear to be in distress . . .

GRAND VIZIER. I am. I am likely to lose my head if I cannot find a boy, an urchin——

ABANAZAR (*with intense sympathy*). Um—um—someone you love ?

GRAND VIZIER. Someone I hate.

ABANAZAR. Why trouble to find him ?

GRAND VIZIER. If I don't somebody else will. If I find him first, I can get him out of the way. (*He makes gesture of throat-cutting.*)

ABANAZAR. Tch-tch ! I begin to understand. Describe him to me.

GRAND VIZIER. I can't. I know nothing about him, except that he is a ragged urchin of this town, who from his behaviour appears to be entirely without fear.

ABANAZAR (*very excited*). What's that ? Without fear ? *I* am looking for a boy without fear. If I find him I promise you that you shall never be troubled with him again. (*Whispering to him.*) Do you know anyone in Peking by the name of Aladdin ?

GRAND VIZIER (*ponders and shakes head*). No, no, I can't say that I do. But here comes the very person to help us. Widow Twankey—she keeps a laundry—she will probably know the name from the laundry marks.

ABANAZAR. Will she tell us ?

GRAND VIZIER. We must win her confidence. Leave it to me—we'll promise her some little gift . . .

ABANAZAR. Right, I will leave it to you. (*They

search their pockets, with no result.) Why not give her the mule ?

GRAND VIZIER. Excellent.

ABANAZAR. I'd better not be seen. A stranger might arouse suspicion. I'll get behind this—— (*He drags the cart forward and stoops down behind it.*)

(*At this moment the curtains half-way down the stage can be drawn, leaving the remainder of the scene to be played as a front scene. This enables the change to the next scene to be commenced.*)

You question her.

(*Enter* WIDOW TWANKEY.)

GRAND VIZIER. Good day, my good woman.

WIDOW. Don't you "my good woman" me. I'm a respectable widow, and I'll trouble you to remember same, Mr. Hoity-Toity.

GRAND VIZIER (*with tremendous dignity*). Take care, take care, woman. I am the Grand Vizier.

WIDOW. Pardon, pardon, your worshipful highness —a little girlish confusion at meeting a real highborn. You know what it is, your highness . . . (*She gushes up to him but meets with no response.*) Ah, a little cold on the south side—— (*She crosses round to his other side. The* GRAND VIZIER *continues to stare out into space.*) And how is Vizering this season ? Laundering is not what it was—no, not what it was. Pardon ? (*Still no response.*) Granted. (*She sees the mule for the first time.*) Oh, what a brute ! (*As the* GRAND VIZIER *shows indignation.*) No, no, your mistake this time, Vizzy. I was alluding to the animal.

(WIDOW *takes an apple from her apron pocket and offers it to the mule, who snaps at it.*)

Here, Vizzy, Vizzy, quick, it's got my hand. Tickle it in the ribs and make it laugh. Quick !

(*The* GRAND VIZIER *does so, the mule laughs, and her hand is released.*)

GRAND VIZIER. Come away, that brute is dangerous. She nearly had your hand off.

WIDOW. Nothing, nothing at all, I assure you. To one accustomed to mangles, a mule bite is a mere "waffle," as one might say. My own fault entirely—every child knows that the apple or piece of sugar should be laid across the palm—so—— (*She illustrates, handing a lump of sugar to the mule, who takes it quietly.*) There you are!

GRAND VIZIER (*who has been intently interested*). You are a remarkable woman, Widow . . . er . . . Widow ——

WIDOW. Twankey. The "K" pronounced "chee" as in kerchief. (*She sneezes.*)

GRAND VIZIER. And you are a brave woman—— (*He is suddenly struck with an idea.*) Brave! Have you a son, Widow Twankey?

WIDOW. I have, Grand Vizier.

GRAND VIZIER. And is he brave like yourself?

(ABANAZAR *shows signs of excitement, popping up his head, etc.*)

Is he fearless?

WIDOW. Fearless? He's that fearless you can do nothing with him. All the children I've ever known have been brought up to shiver in their timbers like decent children ought to do, but not my Aladdin—not Aladdin, oh, no.

GRAND VIZIER } (*one after the other—very quickly*).
ABANAZAR } Aladdin! Aladdin!

WIDOW. Funny! Sounded like an echo. Did you notice it? Listen. (*She repeats.*) Aladdin! (*No answer.*) Where are you?

ABANAZAR (*forgetting himself*). I'm here.

GRAND VIZIER (*hastily*). You don't want your son to come to any harm, do you, Widow Twankey?

WIDOW. Harm?

GRAND VIZIER. Mark my words. Keep him at home—don't give him too long a rope—or he may hang himself. Now remember, I have warned you.

(ABANAZAR *makes frantic signs to the* GRAND VIZIER *and whispers.*)

Oh, by the way, would you care for a mule? You can have that one if you like.

WIDOW. If I like! Oh, your worship, how can I thank you? (*She runs to it and pets it.*)

GRAND VIZIER. Don't thank me, thank your own courage . . . Good day . . . See you soon, I expect, sooner than you think, perhaps.

(*He goes off, with* ABANAZAR *trying to conceal himself behind the* GRAND VIZIER'S *back. They turn at the moment of exit.*)

Oh, by the way, her name's Jasmine.

(*Exit* GRAND VIZIER *and* ABANAZAR.)

SONG *and* DANCE.

WIDOW. When I was a tiny girl,
In party frock and golden curl,
When Mother asked each Christmas Day—
" What gift d'you wish? "—these words I'd say:

Chorus: Please not a hoop,
Please not a ball,
I want just a pet that will come at my call.
A pretty pet
With whom to play,
Just fancy, my wish has come true to-day!

My pet shall spend her days in clover,
And every night when work is over,
I've got two feet—she's got four—
We'll dance as dance ne'er was danced before!

(*Repeat chorus and dance ad lib.*)

(*At finish of song, enter* ALADDIN.)

WIDOW. Ah, there you are, good-for-nothing. See what mother's won.

ALADDIN (*looking fearfully over his shoulder*). Mother, I want to speak to you.

WIDOW. I've no time to listen now. We must get home. Take the laundry cart, I'm going to ride.

ALADDIN. Mother, you can't ride.

WIDOW. How do you know? I had a cousin on my mother's side married a circus rider. I expect it's hereditary.

ALADDIN. Mother, wait a minute. Can you let me have some money?

WIDOW (*preparing to mount*). Never joke about serious things, son.

ALADDIN. I was never so serious in my life. I've got to go away.

WIDOW. Well, you can't. I've never heard such nonsense; why, I've just been given some advice about you. Home's the best place for you; I've been told so. Go away, whoever heard of such a thing!

ALADDIN. But, mother . . .

WIDOW. Now stop it. We'll get some money soon, and then I'll see what we can do. Now we've got a mule, we can have a van, you shall drive it, that will be a nice little change for you. You'll look very classy fetching the dirty laundry from the palace.

ALADDIN. Drive a laundry van to the palace . . . Mother, you don't know what a dreadful thing you are suggesting. To meet the Princess again, like that . . . Oh, I couldn't, I couldn't . . .

WIDOW. Nonsense, there is no such word in the dictionary. Now, come along, help your mum to mount.

(*Business of trying to mount. Music of* "Ride a Cock Horse." WIDOW *falls off, and eventually they harness the mule to the cart and push it off, the* WIDOW *in the cart.*)

Scene 4

Widow Twankey's *Laundry.*

It is furnished poorly, but with a grandfather's clock, mangle, ironing-board, chairs, table, etc. The stage should be arranged with window and door at back, or entrance through curtains that can be opened widely, so that when the curtains are drawn open, or the blinds of the window raised, the desert, which is visible, can be altered to show the palace later in Act II.

If it is possible, the scene of the laundry should be of the Eastern type, with shuttered and sliding walls.

One side of the stage is a door, or a half-door, through which Jasmine *can be visible.*

Laundry cart at corner of stage L.

At the rise of the Curtain, Aladdin *is seated at the table doing the accounts; the* Widow *is ironing, and singing as she works.* Jasmine *has his two front legs in a laundry-tub.*

Aladdin. Mother, I simply can't add up these while you are making that noise.

Widow. Noise, darling? Mother is singing.

Aladdin. There is an awful amount of money owing to us.

Widow (*quite happily*). That's right.

Aladdin. Don't you mind?

Widow. Well, you see, it isn't as if it's our money really. You see, we owe it to someone else, so it's really theirs. Why should we worry?

(*She releases the mule and puts the tub away. The mule goes out of sight.*)

Aladdin. Here is a bill from Hassan the baker.

Widow. Yes, and I'm not going to do another stroke of washing for them until they pay us.

Aladdin. But, mother, this letter says no more bread till we pay them.

Widow. Very well, then, we've nothing for tea. That's all that amounts to.

ALADDIN. Mother, why not do their washing and take bread as payment? You wouldn't need money, then.

WIDOW (*very shocked*). Wouldn't need money? My boy, do you know what you are saying? These sort of things are not done.

ALADDIN. But why not?

WIDOW. Because they're not.

ALADDIN (*illustrating, by putting book on one side, inkpot on other*). Here's the laundry, and here's the bread; and you can't do anything because we haven't any money. It's idiotic!

WIDOW. Now look here, my lad, don't you be getting any new-fangled ideas into your head, and setting yourself up to know better than your elders. What has been must be—and it's not for us to judge.

(DUET—*optional.*)

This iron's too cool. (*She irons with it, then holds up garment with a large hole in it. This is managed by having two garments alike and changing them, unseen by the audience.*) You had better tack a bit of red cotton round this hole. (*She hands* ALADDIN *a large packing-needle threaded with red wool.*)

ALADDIN (*sewing*). Why do you have to do this?

WIDOW. So that they shan't miss the hole. Now then, have you finished those books? (*She clears them away.*)

ALADDIN. Yes, mother.

WIDOW. How much money have we?

ALADDIN. None at all, mother.

WIDOW. Then we shall have to sell the laundry.

ALADDIN. If you did that I could go away, there would be nothing to keep me here.

WIDOW. What's all this talk of wanting to go away? What have you been up to?

ALADDIN. Nothing, mother. Some of our things would fetch a good price. (*He points to the clock.*) Other people in Peking haven't got such things as ours.

WIDOW. They are heirlooms, son. There are secrets about my ancestry that I haven't cared to disclose to everybody. That is an English clock. I wasn't born in Peking. Your mother is not pure Pekinese.

ALADDIN (*eagerly*). Mother, have we royal blood in us? Have we?

WIDOW. Possibly, possibly. I remember your grandfather used to speak of royalty a good deal in the old days. The Royal Oak, the Royal Arms, and he mentioned visiting the Prince of Wales most Saturdays . . .

(*A loud knock at the door interrupts.*)

ALADDIN. You answer it, mother.

WIDOW. What on earth's come to you? (*She opens the door.*)

ABANAZAR (*outside*). Does the Widow Twankey live here?

WIDOW. Well, she does and she doesn't, as the saying goes. She's not at home in any case. (*She tries to shut the door, but* ABANAZAR *puts his foot in.*) Look at that, now.

ABANAZAR. Not to a poor relation?

WIDOW. Never to a poor one; besides, I haven't any relations.

ALADDIN. How do you know, mother?—it might be an ancestor. Let him in. Come in, sir.

(ABANAZAR *enters.*)

ABANAZAR. I have come to seek the widow of my poor brother.

WIDOW. That settles it, my husband never had a brother. He was a twin.

ABANAZAR. A twin. The widow of my twin.

WIDOW. My husband's twin was a sister. A sweet child, little Clarissa . . . I've never forgotten . . . her little head . . . all run over . . .

ABANAZAR. Run over? Automobile?

WIDOW. No, curls. Little head running over with curls . . . We were the spit images of each other. (*She is overcome.*)

ABANAZAR Pardon me, madam, there was another brother. There must have been if I am he.

ALADDIN. Look here, have you any proofs of your identity ?

ABANAZAR. Give me some supper first, young sir, and I will furnish you with all the proofs you need.

WIDOW. We are not troubling about supper to-night. . . . As a matter of fact, I am on a very strict diet . . . slimming.

ALADDIN. Mother, don't pretend . . . Why not tell the truth ? We haven't any food in the house, and we have no money to buy food. We would give you supper with pleasure if we had any, but we have none ourselves.

(ABANAZAR *rubs his ring and mutters the spell.*)

ABANAZAR. Habash ca gruelling—om—ba, Gomish, Habacca !

ALADDIN. What are you saying ?

ABANAZAR. I am saying that you do not speak the truth.

ALADDIN. You had better be careful.

ABANAZAR. I am saying that you have plenty of food concealed . . . if you are so certain, why not go and look in there . . . (*He points to the clock.*) Look, in the clock.

(*In the original production a trick table was used, and if this is done, the following dialogue can be left out. There is a crash and the clock door flies open and* GOMISH *appears for an instant. The table opens and is seen to be full of good things. They seat themselves with exclamations of delight.*

If a simpler method of production is helpful, the following dialogue and business can be used.)

WIDOW
ALADDIN } (*speaking together*). What was that ?

ABANAZAR (*chuckling and pointing to the door*). Open it. Are you afraid ?

ALADDIN (*going to the clock*). I am not afraid, but if you are fooling us you had better beware. (*He opens the door of the clock and takes out a ham.*)

ABANAZAR. We shall want bread. (*He waves his wand over the tub.*)

(WIDOW *takes out a loaf.*)

WIDOW. Oh, my, could we have a bit of fruit?

(*Fruit can be forthcoming from any place that the producer can suggest.*)

Fancy, we'll be having golden plates next!

(*They come rolling on. Eventually the table is set and they seat themselves, and the play goes on from the same point as if they were seated round the trick table.*)

ABANAZAR. It is a pity that I am not your brother-in-law, then I might have stayed with you for a bit. There must be other things you would like.

WIDOW. Who says you're not?

ABANAZAR. You said your husband had no brother.

WIDOW. We all make mistakes sometimes. After all, some people never learn to count. I begin to recognize you with every mouthful.

ALADDIN. I vote he stays, uncle or no uncle. (*He takes wine-flagon.*) This is finer than anything I have ever tasted. Have some, mother?

WIDOW (*rising*). Not for me. If you will excuse me, I'll just go into the kitchen and pop the kettle on. I'm always one for a cup of tea, always have been, and afterwards we'll have a peep at the tea-leaves.

(WIDOW *exits to kitchen.*)

ALADDIN. Who are you really?

ABANAZAR. Would you like me to be your uncle?

ALADDIN. I think I should; perhaps you could help me.

ABANAZAR. I can.

ALADDIN. How do you know what I want?

ABANAZAR. You want what all mankind wants—fame, fortune, and love—happiness and power—but most of all wealth, the key to them all. I can help you to get all these if you trust me.

ALADDIN. If you can do that for me I will trust you. But how do I know you speak the truth?

ABANAZAR (*making a sign over the dish of fruit*). Look at that fruit, look well.

ALADDIN (*taking a jewel out of the dish*). Why, this is not fruit any longer . . . this is a jewel . . . a beauty. Fit for the Princess herself.

ABANAZAR. The Princess is only a girl, she would welcome gifts from you, if they were gifts rich enough to satisfy the Emperor.

ALADDIN. You are right. But where can I get gifts that are rare enough to please an Emperor?

ABANAZAR (*leaning towards him and pointing out of the window*). To-night I have a journey to make. I want a lad to help me. All I ask is that he be strong, willing, obedient, and above all fearless. If you are not afraid, come. Are you afraid?

ALADDIN. Not I.

ABANAZAR. Good. Then I promise you that jewels and wealth beyond your wildest dreams shall be within your reach to-night. The means of getting all the wealth you wish for (*he chuckles evilly*) within your reach . . . I swear it . . . Will you come?

ALADDIN. I will.

(*Noise off stage. The* GRAND VIZIER'S *voice is heard.*)

GRAND VIZIER. Open in the name of the Emperor of all peoples. Open, I say.

ALADDIN. He must not see me. I must hide. If you want me to go with you to-night, don't tell a soul that I am here. (*He conceals himself under the clothes in the laundry cart.*) Cover me up well.

(*Re-enter the* WIDOW.)

WIDOW. What's all this noise?

(*She goes to the door and opens it. The* GRAND VIZIER *enters.*)

Oh, Vizzy, you oughtn't to come here like this. You'll get us talked about. Have you come for the mule?

Grand Vizier. Not on any account, but the Emperor insists that this proclamation be announced all over Peking before nightfall. (*He reads :*) " Inasmuch as the Princess has broken her long silence, and the cause thereof being as expected and according to prophecy, the youth who is suspected of loving and being loved is hereby summoned to the palace to enable the Emperor of all his peoples to keep his promise and celebrate the betrothal of his daughter the beloved and beauteous Badroulbadour." (*He looks round.*) Do you know this lad ? He is suspected of being a common boy, some ragged, impudent urchin . . . Er . . . not your son by any chance ?

Widow. They'd never let the Princess marry a commoner.

Grand Vizier. The Emperor has never broken his promise, and the Princess will be no less attractive for becoming a widow. (*He smiles and makes signs of throat-cutting.*) So. (Widow *shudders.*) It is all arranged—immediately after the ceremony.

Widow. Oh, my kettle ! (*She runs off to the kitchen.*)

Abanazar (*with one eye on cart, making sure he is heard by* Aladdin). If this boy had been wealthy, if he had rare gifts to offer the Emperor ?

Grand Vizier. The Emperor would welcome him with open arms—— (*He suddenly recognizes* Abanazar.) Oh, it's you again ? Well, any news ?

Abanazar (*whispering*). I know where to find him, and where to lose him too.

Grand Vizier. Good. If no one comes forward to make a claim, my son will stand another chance. That is all I care about. If you succeed, great rewards will be yours.

Abanazar (*chuckling*). They will ; you speak truer than you know.

(*Enter* Widow *with teapot.*)

Widow. Making friends ? That's right. How about a nice cup of tea ?

(TRIO.)

Now {I've / she's} put the kettle on,
Have a cup, it won't take long;
Do you like it weak or strong?
Your cup of tea?
Then when we have drunk it up,
Read the tea-leaves in your cup;
See if fortune and good luck
Have come with cups of tea!

(*At the end of the trio they dance, and the* GRAND VIZIER *exits.*)

(*As soon as the coast is clear* ALADDIN *gets out of the cart.*)

Oh, there you are. Come out of that, make yourself tidy, and take the clean laundry up to the palace.

ALADDIN. Mother, I can't. I can never take the laundry up there again. You heard what the Grand Vizier said.

WIDOW. It's no business of yours—(*suddenly a thought comes to her*) unless—oh, you don't mean . . . YOU?

ALADDIN. Now you see why I want to get away. I must . . . If they find me they will only make a mock of us, and execute me afterwards. I must have riches, so I am going with my uncle. He says he can show me where to find them . . . In the meantime, mother, you go up to the palace and take these with you. (*He hands her the fruit-dish.*) Take them to the Emperor as my first gift, and give this message to the Princess: tell her that I am only waiting to make myself worthy; she will understand, she will wait, I know.

WIDOW. Me? Me go to the palace! Oh, I couldn't.

ALADDIN. Oh, mother, do!

WIDOW. But I've nothing to wear.

ALADDIN. There must be something in the laundry that would do . . . (*He searches in the cart and finds a long scarf, or Turkish trousers, or some garment.*)

WIDOW (*taking them and holding them upside down*). These don't look quite right, do they ?

ALADDIN. You've got them the wrong way round. Quick, mother, go and put them on.

(*He bustles the* WIDOW *into the kitchen.*)

Now then, Uncle, come on.

ABANAZAR. We'll take your beast, I don't like walking.

ALADDIN. Right you are. . . . Jasmine, come along . . .

(*The music begins slowly at first, getting gradually faster and faster, till at the end of the song they are all dancing, the* WIDOW *entering and following, doing exaggerated posturings with the bowl of fruit held on her shoulder.*)

With bag and baggage off we go,
Those lovely fruits to him we'll show,
You take the high road, we the low:
We're off to seek our fortune.

ABANAZAR. Now help me up on Jasmine's back—
ALADDIN. Of palace life I'll get the knack—
ALL. Now come on, Jasmine, don't be slack.
We're off to seek our fortune. . . .

(*Repeat ad lib.*)

(*At the end of the song all exit.*)

QUICK CURTAIN.

SCENE 5

Entrance to the Ruby Cave.

This SCENE *shows a blank piece of rock, with, if possible, a section that can open, placed against the curtains forming the front scene.*

Music—and ALHIRA *enters. She dances across the stage, then turns and beckons.*

JASMINE *comes running on. They dance,* ALHIRA *showing by mime that she is leading* JASMINE *away with her. She exits with the mule.*

After a slight pause ALADDIN *comes on, rather breathless, as if he had been chasing the mule.*

ALADDIN. I'm not going any further. I've lost Jasmine, and it looks as if I'd lost uncle. I wonder if he really is my uncle. Every mile we get further away from home, he becomes less like a loving relative, and more like a slave-driver. When we do find this treasure I mean to keep an eye on him. I don't altogether trust him.

(ABANAZAR *enters and clutches* ALADDIN *by the arm.*)

ABANAZAR. Ha, ha, you thought to escape me, did you ?

ALADDIN (*shaking himself free*). What do you mean ? Why should I want to escape you, unless you are other than you pretend to be ? If you want me to go any further you had better be civil. I am tired.

ABANAZAR (*changing his tone and speaking soothingly*). Don't take any notice of your old uncle, lad. I am an old man ; I was a little upset at losing sight of you . . . I was cross and tired . . . have patience—you cannot go to your Princess empty-handed.

ALADDIN. You keep on saying that, but nothing ever happens. Well, lead on, and be quick about it.

ABANAZAR (*who has been peering about*). There is no need to go on, we are there.

ALADDIN. This gloomy spot ? This doesn't appear very promising. I can see nothing but a blank wall.

(ABANAZAR *takes no notice of him, but proceeds to draw circles on the ground with his stick, muttering to himself.*)

ALADDIN. What are you doing ? Do you know I am beginning to be . . .

ABANAZAR (*hastily interrupting him*). Don't, don't say it.

ALADDIN. I shall say what I like. I am tired of you, and I am getting a little bit . . .

(ABANAZAR *stuffs his fingers in his ears.*)

suspicious of all this.

ABANAZAR (*beaming at him*). Oh, only suspicious? I thought you were going to say afraid.

ALADDIN. Afraid? I'm not afraid of you.

ABANAZAR. What a blessing! (*He resumes his muttering and waves his stick, going slowly round and round in a circle.*)

(*The entrance to the cave begins to open.*)

ALADDIN. Uncle, look! Look what is happening!

ABANAZAR. It's not happening—I am doing it.

(*The cave opens.*)

Now go in.

ALADDIN. In there?

ABANAZAR. Yes, yes, go . . . go quickly.

ALADDIN (*very interested, he looks in*). All right, don't be in such a hurry. It's a bit surprising. You see, rocks don't do that as a rule, do they? Are you coming too?

ABANAZAR (*shrinking back*). No, no, I cannot. Go down the steps, do not linger one moment longer than you need—in a niche by the ruby rock you will see a lamp. Bring it to me. . . . (*His voice becomes eager and trembles with excitement.*) Bring me the lamp—go, go . . . Are you going, or are you not?

ALADDIN. Of course I am going, don't get so upset. There's heaps of time. Of course I'll go.

ECHO (*voices off stage*). He'll go.

ALADDIN. Why, it's an echo.

ECHO. Echo!

ALADDIN. That's jolly.

ECHO. Jolly.

ALADDIN. It's like having a lot of friends—like going to a party.

(ECHO SONG—*with chorus.*)

As you gaily go upon your way,
Voices will call you.
So just be careful what you think or say,
Echo answers to you!
When your heart is merry, you will hear a song,
Echo will sing you,
But if you're sorry, and your face is long—
Echo answers to you!

Echo is calling,
Echo is calling,
Echo comes our steps to greet—
Echo is calling,
Echo is calling,
Echo is calling so sweet!

(*At the end of the song,* ALADDIN *enters the cave, and during repetition of chorus the lights go down, and the curtains are drawn, disclosing the interior of the Ruby Cave.*)

SCENE 6

Inside the Ruby Cave.

Entrance to the cave on one side of the stage. If possible a flight of steps. The cave is empty except for rocks and jewels (see Note on Scenery), and the lamp which stands in one corner, and one or two jars full of precious stones.

At the rise of the CURTAIN *the echo song continues, and the jewels are dancing. There is a noise off stage.* ALADDIN'S *voice is heard and they disperse.*

ALADDIN *appears in the entrance.*

ALADDIN. How quiet it is now that the echo has died away. It would be quite dark if those jewels did not sparkle so. How lovely they are! I must take plenty away with me. (*He looks round.*) Oh, aren't they marvellous? I know, I must get that bag of uncle's. I wish he would come down, it's a bit creepy here all alone. (*He calls:*) Uncle, uncle!

ECHO. Uncle, uncle!

ABANAZAR (*appearing at the entrance*). What is it? Stop making all that noise, and hurry. Can you see the lamp? Can you see it?

ALADDIN. No. (*Angry sound from* ABANAZAR.) Wait a minute, there is so much to look at. These jewels are wonderful. I say, uncle, fetch me your bag, I want it to put them in. (ALADDIN *busies himself taking jewels from the jar.*)

ABANAZAR. Give me the lamp.

ALADDIN. Get me the bag.

ABANAZAR. The bag is here . . . the lamp . . . tell me, is it there?

ALADDIN. Bother the lamp . . . no . . . yes, here it is. I'll bring it and fetch the bag . . .

(*He goes up to the entrance and holds out his arm for the bag.* ABANAZAR *tries to snatch at the lamp, and* ALADDIN *nearly overbalances. He stumbles and clutches at the bag,* ABANAZAR *pushes him away.* ALADDIN *falls, but still retains the lamp.*)

(*Sitting on the ground and rubbing himself.*) Here, what are you doing? (*To himself.*) That was funny. I could almost believe that uncle tried to push me down. (*He sees the lamp.*) Oh, I've still got you, have I? Serve uncle right, there was something horrid in the way he snatched at it. This time, I'll jolly well get the jewels and get outside before I give it to him again. I'll have a joke with him. I'll make him think I mean to keep it. (*He laughs.*)

(ECHO *laughs also.*)

This place sounds bewitched. (*He gathers up the bag, etc.*)

ABANAZAR. Aladdin, are you all right?

ALADDIN. No, thanks to you.

ABANAZAR. Where is the lamp?

ALADDIN. Here, and here it stays until I am ready.

(*Hooks it on to his belt.*) Now then, (*going to entrance*) you take the bag, and I'll keep the lamp. When I see my jewels safely outside I'll follow, and I'll give you the lamp when you tell me why you want it in such a hurry. (ABANAZAR *holds out his hands, and* ALADDIN *thrusts the bag at him.*) No, no, you take the bag; you shall have the lamp when I am outside.

ABANAZAR (*beside himself with rage*). That you never shall be. Foolish boy! To think you can outwit me! Your fate be on your own head . . . Farewell! Ha, ha, ha!

(*The echoes take up the cry, and* ABANAZAR'S *laugh is echoed. There is a crash to indicate that the cave has closed.* ALADDIN *puts his hand to his ears, as the mocking laugh appears to be all around him. Then at the crash he rushes to the entrance and hammers on the rock.*)

ALADDIN. Uncle, let me out, let me out! I was only joking. You can have the beastly lamp . . . of course you can . . . (*He hammers, and then realizes that there is no result, so he returns to the cave slowly.*) Well, that's a pretty kettle of fish. What is the use of all these jewels if I cannot get out of this place? I wonder if there is another entrance. (*He looks round.*) No, rock everywhere, and jewels. Oh, well, I must just resign myself, I suppose. Perhaps uncle will relent: if not I shall starve; and after such a good supper with him, I shall probably starve very slowly. (*He sits on the ground and sighs.* ECHO *sighs also.*) That sounds as if someone else was sorry for me. Funny place this . . . (*He remembers the lamp.*) What a dirty-looking object to lose one's life for . . . I wonder what it is made of? I'll clean it up a bit . . .

(*He rubs the lamp on his sleeve, and falls backwards in surprise as* ALHIRA *appears.*)

ALHIRA. I thought you were never going to do it. (*She throws herself at his feet.*) Oh, master! (*She puts her arms round his ankles.*)

ALADDIN (*stepping out of them*). I say, how did you get in ?

ALHIRA (*leaping into the air with glee*). You summoned me.

ALADDIN. I did ? Who on earth are you ?

ALHIRA. Your slave, your willing slave . . . (*She again makes a sweeping bow and kneels at his feet.*)

ALADDIN (*very embarrassed*). Now look here, do get up . . . it would be very good of you if you would explain . . .

ALHIRA. I will explain everything . . . all the wisdom of the universe, (*she makes large movements with her arms*) all the vast knowledge of the sages, to my beloved master I can expound all the . . .

ALADDIN (*interrupting her*). No, no, I assure you, if you don't mind, just one tiny little item of information is all that I require. (ALHIRA *makes another sweeping gesture.*) Don't do that again if you don't mind . . . What I want to know is, why did my uncle Abanazar want this (*holding out the lamp*) so much ?

ALHIRA. He did not want the lamp, he wanted *me*.

ALADDIN. Whatever for ? Oh, I don't mean to be rude, but—I mean—why ?

ALHIRA (*with great pride*). I am Alhira, the slave of the lamp. I grant his every behest.

ALADDIN. His every—I say, can you do that ?

ALHIRA. Fearless one, I can. He who owns the lamp can have every wish fulfilled. I am tired of serving greed and hate, now I will serve you. You must have lots of wishes, you are in love.

ALADDIN. How do you know ? Are you in love too ?

ALHIRA. To fall in love is silly. Only mortals do that. We love everything, that is fun. Rub the lamp.

ALADDIN. Rub it ? Is that all I have to do ? (*He laughs.*) I say, it's easy, isn't it ? Slave of the lamp, open that door ! (*The door opens.*) Good gracious, you've done it ! I never thought you really meant it. What fun we're going to have ! Let's get back. (*He rubs the lamp.*) Home, please. Oh, I know, first we must have something to carry all these—of course—a beast of burden . . . (*He rubs the lamp.*) Alhira, a beast of burden, please, to carry my jewels!

(JASMINE *looks in.*)

Jasmine! I say, Alhira, these (*indicating his ragged clothes*) won't look very dressy to arrive in, will they? What about a new suit? (ALHIRA *nods.*) Alhira, robes!

(*Music commences, and jewels dance on, bringing rich garments for* ALADDIN. *He slips away and changes while the dance is going on. At the end of the dance he reappears.*)

Alhira, transport us back to Peking. I will go to the Emperor and demand the hand of his daughter, the beautiful Badroulbadour.

(ALADDIN *leads* JASMINE. *Echo chorus repeated, and all are about to exit as*

The CURTAIN *falls.*

ACT II

Scene 1

A Corner of the Street, Peking.

(Front Scene.)

A crowd of citizens, etc., walk about the stage, chatting together.

Gossiping Chorus.

We gossy-gossip round the town.
Plees on our gossip do not frown, do not frown.
Ze newesy—news of land or air or sea—
I tell it you as told to me.

(Shaking hands with themselves in Chinese fashion.)

How-de-do, plees don't repeat it,
How-de-do, 'twas velly secret.
Plees remember that I trust you not to tell a soul!
How-do? How-do-de-do-dy-do, how-de-do?
Me velly plees to introduce you, to you—to you—
You wish ze news? At dinner, breakfast, tea?
You only haf to tell it me!

(At the end of the chorus the three boys separate themselves from the others, who gradually exit as their lines are finished.)

1st Boy. What can have happened to Aladdin?

2nd Boy. Some say that it was Aladdin himself who made the Princess speak.

3rd Boy. Do you think it is true?

1st Boy. Not likely.

SHOPKEEPER'S WIFE. What's that? Have they found the boy who did it?

1ST BOY. No.

WIFE. I hope they will, I'm looking forward to the festivities.

SHOPKEEPER. They say that even if they don't find the stranger, the betrothal will go on just the same. The Grand Vizier will marry his son to the Princess.

WIFE. I don't care who marries as long as we have the festivities . . .

SHOPKEEPER. If you were the bride you might be more particular!

(*They exit together, laughing.*)

1ST BOY. Come on, there's no use wasting time here.

(*The boys run off together.*)

(*The three maids-in-waiting have entered during this last scene.*)

SING HI (*giving a note to* SING LOH-HI). Quick, take this, Pekoe gave it to me this morning as we passed the Emperor's guard. Oh, I do hope they don't marry him to the Princess.

SING LOH-HI (*glancing at the note*). He wants me to meet him here, later. Oh, Sing Hi, dare I? If the Princess found out!

SING TUH. I don't believe she'd mind, now she's in love herself.

SING LOH-HI. I wish we could help her. If only we had taken more notice of the boy.

SING TUH. It's a lesson not to be *too* obedient another time. We ought to have peeped.

SING LOH-HI. I was too frightened to do anything but obey the Princess. Oh, to be free!

(TRIO—THREE MAIDENS.)

Maidens who serve at court
Have to do as they are taught.
Pleasures are but dearly bought,
And slow the days pass by.

Chorus.

Love should his gifts bestow
On high as well as low.
Why should maids as fair as we
Be left repining so?

Maidens, let us garlands lay
Upon the temple steps, and pray
That Cupid's arrow may not stray
If aimed at one of us.

(*Repeat chorus.*)

(*If preferred others can stroll back and join in this chorus, at the end of which maidens and others all exit.*)

(*When the stage is empty, enter* ABANAZAR, *looking very dejected.*)

ABANAZAR. Nobody here? I told Gomish to see that the Grand Vizier awaited me. Everything else has gone wrong. I hope Gomish hasn't played me false. At least I have got rid of that brat of a boy, and I must see to it that the Grand Vizier rewards me well for that. Aladdin will never see the light of day again. . . . Curse the lamp, I wish I'd never bothered about it. Only my gold is not enough down here. I want position, power——

(GOMISH *enters. He makes a sign indicating that someone is following him. Almost immediately the* GRAND VIZIER *enters, obviously under the influence of a spell. When he gets to the* C. *of the stage,* GOMISH *makes a sign, and the* GRAND VIZIER *wakes with a start.* GOMISH *exits.*)

GRAND VIZIER (*seeing* ABANAZAR). Well, this is odd! I was thinking of you, and I had no intention of coming this way at all. I thought I was on my way to the palace. Well, what news?

ABANAZAR. The boy is out of the way. I have kept *my* promise.

GRAND VIZIER. You are sure he cannot come back?

ABANAZAR. Quite sure, I have left him where . . .

GRAND VIZIER. No, don't give me any details, I am too tender-hearted. Come and see me after the Princess is betrothed to my son and I will keep *my* promise.

ABANAZAR. You won't fail me?

GRAND VIZIER. Trust me. I am so happy I could refuse you nothing. My son need never do another stroke of work; there will be some nice little jobs going at the court. What sort of post would you prefer? Royal egg collector? Boot cleaner to the Royal Guard? Very lucrative, and as they don't wear boots, not overworked. Think it over my boy, think it over!

(DUET—*optional.*)

(*Exit* GRAND VIZIER.)

ABANAZAR. Someone is coming this way. Who can it be, unattended at this hour? It looks like the royal litter-bearers . . Well, I had better accustom myself to the society of these pampered pets of the court . . .

(*The litter is carried on by* LONKA *and* CHORTA *and set down. The curtains are closed.*)

I will peep.

(*A hand is put out.*)

She has taken a fancy to me, I think.

WIDOW (*opening the curtains*). Oh, Abby, is that you? (ABANAZAR *is disappointed.*) How nice of you to come and meet me. They made such a fuss of me up at the palace. Insisted on my coming home in this. (*She gets out, the boys hold out their hands for money.*) What? Money? Oh, no, nothing in the least like that. I tell you what, I'll do a bit of washing for you any time, for nothing, or next to nothing. (*She plucks at his sleeve.*) That ought to iron up nicely . . . Any time you're passing . . .

(LONKA *and* CHORTA *go off with the litter.*)

Well, Abanazar, and how did you leave my Aladdin?

ABANAZAR. Altogether. You'll not see that fool again.

WIDOW. You surprise me, he is generally so regular with his meals.

ABANAZAR. You'll never see him again.

WIDOW. If I thought you meant that, ducky, I'd be crying my eyes out, instead of taking you home to a dish of tea.

ABANAZAR. I am not coming home with you any more.

WIDOW. Oh, yes, you are! I am not letting you out of my sight until I know what you have done with my Aladdin.

(ABANAZAR *rubs his ring violently.* GOMISH *enters suddenly.*)

Oh, who is your little friend? Nasty expression, don't you think? (GOMISH *is snarling at her.*)

ABANAZAR. Gomish, halla zasta draculata holl-a! Get rid of this woman.

WIDOW. Get rid of me? Not he.

ABANAZAR. Gomish, haracka!

GOMISH. Master, I will plague her with the first female torture . . . Mice . . . (*He takes a handful of small mice out of his pocket and holds them threateningly towards the* WIDOW.) Creepy-crawly-running-swiftly-miz-z-z-ze!

WIDOW (*not a bit frightened, but politely interested*). Oh, what are those?

ABANAZAR. If you do not leave us, instantly, I will speak the word and Gomish shall release those mice. They will run about the floor, round your feet.

WIDOW. They'd enjoy that. Do you know, mice always take to me, I think it must be the soap. Anyway, it will be better for them than being crumpled up like that in his pocket. All crunched anyhow! Now, take care, my little man, you've dropped one. (*She picks up one that has escaped and strokes it, then gives it back to* GOMISH *and shoos him off, shaking her apron at him.*) Now be off with you.

(GOMISH *exits discomfited.*)

Aren't you a teeny bit old-fashioned, Abby? While you have been thinking about nothing but gold, women have been growing intelligent. Now come along. When you've had your tea, there's a bit of ironing wants doing, and you can do a bit of washing for me too. Now Aladdin's away I shall need a bit of extra help in the laundry. (*She speaks to him in the tone of one addressing a very small child.*) Now come along, and don't lag.

(*They exit,* ABANAZAR *very unwillingly.*)

(*Enter* PEKOE *and* SING LOH-HI, *from opposite sides of the stage.*)

PEKOE. Loh-Hi, at last!

SING LOH-HI. Pekoe, I am so frightened. Have they any news of the boy who made the Princess speak?

PEKOE. No, I am hoping that he may turn up at the last moment.

SING LOH-HI. I wish I had looked at him carefully, but he seemed just like any of the others. A woman came to the palace and brought beautiful presents for the Emperor. She was so heavily veiled, we could not see her face, but I believe she brought a word of hope to the Princess, who sits gazing across the desert with a sad little smile upon her lips, watching and waiting.

PEKOE. Whatever happens, dear, I am yours, and you must be mine. I could not bear to be parted.

DUET.

1.

SING LOH-HI. Distance to love lends
Enchantment, they say
Love will grow stronger,
If driven away.

PEKOE. I do not see, dear,
How that can be,
If lovers love, dear,
As I love thee.

2.

PEKOE. The one that I love, I would
Talk with each day:
Walk with her, work with her,
Join in her play.

SING LOH-HI. If love loves parting
You may depend
It will grow wings, and
Fly off in the end.

3.

BOTH. Love to which distance
Enchantment can bring,
Is not the love of which
True lovers sing.
How could the love that is
Filling my heart
Grow any deeper
Because we're apart?

(*Exit as* CURTAIN *falls.*)

SCENE 2

WIDOW TWANKEY'S *Laundry.*

ABANAZAR *is washing clothes in the laundry tub.* WIDOW TWANKEY *is ironing.*

DUET.

(*At the end of the duet a loud angry knocking is heard.*)

SHOPKEEPER'S WIFE (*speaking outside*). Can I come in, Mrs. Twankey?

WIDOW. Oh, it's you, is it? Come in.

(*Enter the* SHOPKEEPER'S WIFE, *in a great state of mind. She is waving two differently coloured stockings.*)

WIFE. Look at these!

WIDOW. They don't seem to take after each other,

do they ? I should say they was odd. Yes, that's right. That's what they are—odd.

WIFE. You can't put me off like that. I demand the others.

WIDOW. We must look for them.

WIFE. You'd better. You find them.

WIDOW. Find ? Oh, looking and finding are two different things. I said nothing about finding them. I don't suppose we'll do that.

WIFE. I shall not pay your bill.

WIDOW. Now where have I heard that before ? Somebody said it . . . (*Smiling pleasantly.*) Funny you should use the very same words.

WIFE. I don't care who said it. I say it, and I say it to you, and I mean it. You send me those stockings, or no money of mine do you see, or touch. Remember that ! No money of mine . . . no money of mine . . . not one penny . . .

(*She exits, talking violently, and you hear her voice dying away in the distance.*)

ABANAZAR. What's for supper ?

WIDOW. Bread and cheese, and be thankful.

ABANAZAR. Why not those sausages ? (*He points to a string of sausages hanging on the wall.*)

WIDOW. I am keeping those till Aladdin comes back.

ABANAZAR. Buy some more, I can give you gold.

WIDOW. Certainly not; you can't appear with money suddenly in this world unless you can explain where you got it from. Where do you get it from ?

ABANAZAR. I've told you. I make it.

WIDOW. I can't believe that. 'Tisn't as if you were a highborn, or a banker, or something classy like that.

ABANAZAR. If I were a banker, would you let me have sausages for tea ?

WIDOW. Ah, if you were a banker you could let me have an overdraft. That's respectable, and then we might—mind, I don't say we would, but we might stretch to a relish for tea. (*She goes to the window.*) I do wish Aladdin was at home.

ABANAZAR. Do stop thinking of that brat.

WIDOW. I can't. Oh, where is my wandering boy to-night ?

(*There is a sound of hoofs galloping.*)

ALADDIN (*outside*). Mother ! Mother !

WIDOW. Aladdin !

ABANAZAR. I'm too late . . . foiled again !

(ALADDIN *enters, in his new rich dress, followed by* JASMINE *laden with bags of jewels, and with a wonderful jewelled head-dress and harness.*)

ALADDIN (*embracing his mother*). Mother, how glad I am to be back again. (*He sees* ABANAZAR.) That villain here ? Mother, he is the man who tried to take my life. (*To* ABANAZAR.) Out you go, not another moment do you spend under this roof.

(ABANAZAR *creeps round to the door, trying to snatch sausages as he passes.*)

WIDOW. Look out, Aladdin, he is trying to take our sausages !

ALADDIN. We don't want him, or his sausages. (*He throws them after* ABANAZAR.) I can get you all you need now, mother. All our troubles are over. Look at me.

WIDOW. Aren't you splendid ? Oh, wherever did you get those clothes ? (*She examines them.*) Show the dirt a bit, won't they ? Did they cost a lot ? (*She sees* JASMINE's *decorations.*) Oh, Jasmine, what have you been up to ?

(*The mule trots inside.*)

ALADDIN. Tell me first, mother, what did the Emperor say to our gifts ? Did he accept them ?

WIDOW. Did he not ? But, Aladdin, he wasn't satisfied. He says he must have proof that you can keep his daughter in the state to which she has become accustomed.

ALADDIN. Is that all? (*He laughs.*) I'll show him.

WIDOW (*with deep anxiety*). My boy, you don't have headaches or anything, do you? Don't see things? Or anything like that? No pain? (*He laughs and shakes his head.*) Aladdin, I'm frightened; give it all up and come back to the laundry and mother.

ALADDIN. Nonsense, mother. I must marry the Princess. Don't worry, I have a secret which I must guard, but we shall have all we need. You go to bed, leave it all to me, and trust me.

WIDOW. All right, son, good night. Put out the lights and lock up. Oh, and leave the empty milk bottles outside . . . Oh, and don't sit up too late . . . Oh, and don't read, it's not good for your eyes . . .

(*She exits, talking all the time, speaking the last directions as she is just off stage.*)

(ALADDIN *looks at the magic lamp.*)

ALADDIN. I'll keep you safely. I wonder what Badroulbadour is doing at this moment. Is she thinking of me? I wonder if I could find out. Perhaps Alhira could tell me.

(ALADDIN *rubs the lamp.*)

(ALHIRA *appears in the doorway.*)

Alhira, I am feeling rather sad and lonely. Find out if the Princess is thinking of me?

ALHIRA. Why not ask her for yourself?

ALADDIN. I wish I could, but how can I?

ALHIRA. Would that be your wish, master?

(ALADDIN *walks about the room.* ALHIRA *disappears.*)

ALADDIN. Oh, it would be wonderful, just to open that door and find the Princess outside. Alhira . . . Why, she's gone . . . Alhira!

(*There is a single knock on the door.* ALADDIN *is startled.*)

What was that?

(*Two little rat-tats are heard.* ALADDIN *strides to the*

door and opens it. The PRINCESS *is standing outside.* ALADDIN *steps back a little, hardly believing his eyes.*)

Princess!

PRINCESS. Aladdin, do ask me to come in.

ALADDIN (*falling on one knee and kissing her hand*). Princess! (*He leads her into the room.*) How did you come here?

PRINCESS. I don't know. I was sitting at my window, wondering whether I should ever see you again. My father was arguing with me, trying to persuade me to marry the Grand Vizier's son. I was so bored, wishing I might be with you, and suddenly—here I was. (*She looks round the room.*) Is this where you live?

ALADDIN. Yes. Oh, Princess, it is wonderful to see you here, at home.

PRINCESS. This doesn't look very like a home to me. (*She points to the mangle.*) What is that strange decorative thing?

ALADDIN. That is a mangle, Princess. You see, this is a laundry as well as a home. We are only poor people—at least, we were. Now I am rich—I can give you a palace fit for you, that will satisfy even the Emperor.

PRINCESS. I wouldn't mind a bit, Aladdin, only I do think my father will expect something a little different from this. (*She waves her fan to indicate the signs of poverty.*)

ALADDIN. I can fulfil all his expectations.

PRINCESS. Can you, Aladdin? Can you really do all you say? Oh, I do hope that you can.

ALADDIN. Only trust me, Princess.

PRINCESS. I will. (*They embrace.*) Look out there, (*she points to the window*) across the desert, how dark and silent it is. I wish we could steal away there together.

(ALADDIN *draws the curtains.*)

ALADDIN. Let's pretend we are married, and all the fuss is over. Let's pretend.

(DUET.)

(*At the end of the duet there is a loud knocking at the door.*)

PRINCESS. Aladdin, what is that?

LONKA, CHORTA, LONKA, EMPEROR (*outside*).
LONKA. Open!
CHORTA. In the name of the Emperor.
LONKA. Open!
EMPEROR. Why do they not obey?

PRINCESS. My father's voice! Aladdin, I am terrified! He has followed me.

ALADDIN. But how could he know that you were here?

PRINCESS (*with a little cry*). Oh, look, see, there is rice upon the floor! Oh, Aladdin, see, they sewed this little bag of rice inside the hem of my dress. At every footfall, a grain of rice has marked the way I came. Oh, my father will have you killed.

LONKA. Open—

CHORTA. In the name of the Emperor—

LONKA. Open!

(ALADDIN *opens the door.* LONKA *and* CHORTA *enter, followed by the* EMPEROR, GRAND VIZIER, PEKOE *and* MAIDENS. ALADDIN *kneels with the* PRINCESS.)

(SONG: EMPEROR.)

Aha, I am an Emperor,
So tremble all Peking.
My rank is much superior
To an ordinary king.

CHORUS. And when an Emperor's voice is heard,
Let every voice be dumb—

EMPEROR. My voice is so superior
And would be were I dumb.
An Emperor has to rule his land,
From dawn to set of sun,
And if his brain get out of hand
He rules by rule of thumb.

(*He turns his thumbs down, all shudder.*)

EMPEROR. What is the meaning of this insult to my house? I find the sacred head of the most royal of princesses under the poverty-stricken roof of an ignorant laundryman. A commoner!

LONKA. His mother launders also——

CHORTA. Indifferent ironer.

ALADDIN. Hold your tongues.

GRAND VIZIER. You will never be able to hold yours again, it's going to be cut out.

EMPEROR (*to the crowd in general*). Silence! Now, daughter.

PRINCESS (*crossing over to him*). Father, have mercy. Aladdin didn't ask me to come. I wished it so much that I found myself here. I don't know how.

GRAND VIZIER (*with a loud snort*). Pshaw!

EMPEROR (*who has turned to him for advice*). Pshaw! A likely tale.

(WIDOW *rushes on in a dressing-gown.*)

WIDOW. What's all this? Such goings on at this time of night I cannot have. Aladdin, if you must invite your Bohemian friends . . .

PRINCESS. Hush, if you are his mother, down on your knees, and plead for your son's life. Don't anger the Emperor more. . . .

WIDOW. The Emp . . . lor' lovey! (*She drops on her knees with a bump.*)

EMPEROR (*peering at the* WIDOW). That is the woman who brought me the jewels. They were very fine ones, too. You seem to have forgotten them, Vizier. (*He beams at the* WIDOW.) I remember that you besought my favour for your son. Is this the lad?

PRINCESS	(*all speaking together*).	Yes, father, and you must ——
GRAND VIZIER		Emperor, you must not listen——
PEKOE		Indeed it is, and it might be advisable——
WIDOW		Yes, indeed the best son that ever——
ALADDIN		Indeed, if you will but let me prove——

EMPEROR. Silence! Is anyone trying to give advice to the Emperor of all the stars?

ALL. Majesty, no, no, a thousand times no!

GRAND VIZIER. Most beautiful, listen. This boy and his mother have bewitched us. He is a common lad. Jewels may be all very well, but the Princess cannot live on jewels, she cannot eat them.

EMPEROR (*nodding*). True, that is true.

PEKOE. But she can wear them (*the* EMPEROR *stares at him*) with other things as well, of course, Emperor.

GRAND VIZIER. But if in the great generosity of your merciful bounty you consented to a betrothal, where would the Princess live, sleep, eat? In this hovel? In this squalid hole?

WIDOW (*preparing for a fight by turning up her sleeves*). Does he mean our house, Aladdin?

(ALADDIN *motions to her to be quiet.*)

EMPEROR. True—— (*He nods again.*) True. What do you suggest?

GRAND VIZIER. Chop off his head, save yourself any further trouble.

EMPEROR. That possibly would be best.

PRINCESS. Father, do you wish me to be dumb again?

EMPEROR (*startled*). What? No, no, of course not.

PRINCESS. I trust Aladdin, I believe what he has told me. If he can find me no home that is befitting my rank and title, then I will accept any fate you may decide for me, but he must have a chance. If you will not listen to him, I will never open my lips to ask a boon again, nor ever speak one solitary word.

EMPEROR. I hate being badgered, my word ought to be supreme. (*He appeals to the* GRAND VIZIER.) You see how I am placed? (*The* GRAND VIZIER *shrugs an assent.*) Well, then, so be it. (*To* ALADDIN.) Speak.

ALADDIN (*to* PRINCESS). Your faith has saved us. Emperor, I have a palace in my mind, more beautiful than any yet seen.

EMPEROR (*sneering*). In your mind ?

ALADDIN. The walls of marble and precious stones enclose treasures more wonderful than all the wealth of Old Peking would buy. Give me your daughter, and I will promise that her days shall be composed of all the sweet delights that poets have sung through all the ages. She shall bathe in pools of glistening silver water——

WIDOW (*in a loud whisper*). Mind the stinging nettles, dearie.

ALADDIN (*taking no notice*). She shall dine off tables and dishes of purest gold—her couch shall be of rarest gems—jasper, onyx, opals and lapis lazuli——

GRAND VIZIER (*to himself*). A bit nobbly !

ALADDIN. Ten thousand slaves shall wait upon her slightest whim, and bring her robes of fairest silk—flaming rubies to match her lips, and softly tinted weavings to enrich the beauty of her hair and eyes. Where, O Emperor, where is a gift equal to the one my love brings with it ?

EMPEROR. You speak well, young man, and I am not adverse to these enticements, but . . .

GRAND VIZIER. Where are they, Emperor ?

EMPEROR. Exactly, where ? Words will not build a palace.

PRINCESS (*very sadly*). My father speaks truly, where is this palace ?

WIDOW. Don't look at me, dearie, the boy's mad.

PRINCESS. Oh, if it were only true ! (*She buries her face in the* WIDOW'S *shoulder.*)

(ALADDIN *rubs the lamp.*)

ALADDIN (*calling*). Alhira.

(ALHIRA *appears. She makes a gesture and walks slowly up to the back of the stage. The crowd stand back amazed to see her. All watch her intently.*)

Slave of the lamp, quickly, my palace ! The palace of our dreams !

ALHIRA (*standing with outstretched arms*). Master, it is here.

ALADDIN. Come, Princess, have courage. (*He holds out his hand and leads the* PRINCESS *to the back of the stage, the curtain is parted, and the palace is seen in the distance.*)

ALL. Look, look, a palace!

1ST. (*all speak together*). A palace has sprung up in a moment!
2ND. A palace! 'Tis magic!
3RD. Majesty, Majesty, a palace!
GRAND VIZIER. Curse the boy. A palace!

PEKOE *and* SING LOH-HI. We are saved!
Oh, Pekoe, we shall be free!

EMPEROR. If the inside be half as worthy as the outer, then indeed I will keep my word—the Princess shall be yours.

ALADDIN. Alhira, lead the way. Come, Princess, no more fears, come to the palace of our dreams.

Chorus.

Come ye to our palace,
It's towers reach the sky,
Lights above gleam bright, like
Sparks that upward fly.
Come then to our palace,
The palace of our dream,
A palace so magnificent,
Has surely ne'er been seen!

(*During the singing of the chorus, all leave the stage two by two, pointing towards the palace as they go.* ALADDIN *and the* PRINCESS *are the last to leave the stage; as they reach the exit the curtains close across the stage to form a front scene.*)

The music becomes faster, and the couples enter in the same order, and hurry across the stage, pointing ahead in a state of great excitement.

ALADDIN *and the* PRINCESS *are again the last to exit, and as they do so*

The CURTAIN *falls.*

SCENE 3

The Street Again.

There is a single lamp in the C. *of the stage. Imitation street lamp with lantern on it.*

(*Enter* ABANAZAR, *walking slowly and looking very disconsolate. He carries a small sack.*)

ABANAZAR. Everyone is invited to the palace to-morrow, except me. But I intend to have revenge. I have a plan that will foil all their hopes. Here in this sack I have collected all the bright new lamps in Peking. When I go round calling out, " New lamps for old—New lamps for old," the proud Princess will fall into the trap I have laid for her easily enough. (*He peers round.*) Nobody about—I hoped I should run into Widow Twankey. I'll hang around a bit. I won't go too near that light, I don't want to be noticed. (*He seats himself in one corner of the stage, facing the corner.*)

(*Enter the* GRAND VIZIER.)

GRAND VIZIER. Of course I'm invited to the palace to-morrow. (*He peers around, but does not see* ABANAZAR.) I asked Pekoe to meet me here, but it's so dark I can't see an inch in front of my nose. I won't go too near that light, it doesn't do to be seen hanging about. (*He sits in the opposite corner of the stage to* ABANAZAR, *facing into the corner.*)

(PEKOE *and the* WIDOW *enter at the same moment from opposite sides of the stage. The* WIDOW *same side as* ABANAZAR, PEKOE *the same side as the* GRAND VIZIER.)

ABANAZAR. Widow Twankey, do stop a moment.

GRAND VIZIER (*speaking almost at the same moment to* PEKOE). Hi, Pekoe, here I am, come and talk to me.

WIDOW (*to* ABANAZAR). Under protest, under protest, mind. (*She sits by* ABANAZAR.)

GRAND VIZIER (*speaking rather crossly, thinking that*

PEKOE *answered him*). Under protest? That is hardly a polite way to address your father.

PEKOE (*protesting*). Father, I don't know what you mean, I did not speak. I want to tell you . . . (*He talks to the* GRAND VIZIER *in an undertone.*)

WIDOW. Come back to the laundry? I am afraid you can't . . .

ABANAZAR. But listen to me . . .

(*They argue softly together.*)

PEKOE. Father, I shall not be unhappy.

GRAND VIZIER. Not unhappy, when that upstart is marrying the Princess?

PEKOE. I shall be marrying the girl I love. Father, do give me your consent.

WIDOW (*loudly*). Certainly not, certainly not.

PEKOE (*thinking the* GRAND VIZIER *spoke*). If that is your answer I shall leave home for ever.

GRAND VIZIER. I gave no answer, do give your old father time to think. I only want your happiness. I know I am . . .

ABANAZAR. A fool, an old fool!

GRAND VIZIER (*to* PEKOE). How dare you say such a thing?

PEKOE. I never said a word, this place is bewitched! (*They all get up in anger and see one another.*)

GRAND VIZIER (*to* ABANAZAR). Oh, it's you, is it! Run away, my son, I want a word with this friend of mine. Oh, go on—do as you like. Yes, I consent, have it your own way.

PEKOE. Thank you, father. I will go and give the good news to Loh-Hi.

(*Exit* PEKOE.)

GRAND VIZIER (*to* ABANAZAR). Causing trouble as usual?

ABANAZAR (*looking at the* WIDOW *with meaning*). Two's company.

GRAND VIZIER (*taking the* WIDOW'S *arm*). Quite right. Have you counted us?

WIDOW. Now, boys, don't quarrel.

ABANAZAR. Why can't I come back to the laundry? It is dangerous to refuse me, I miss my sausage teas.

WIDOW. That's only cupboard love. Besides, I am a personage now. I am going into high society. Am I not, Grand Vizier?

GRAND VIZIER. Aladdin's mother is bound to be a social success.

WIDOW. Not yet, but I shall be; I am studying the social arts, (*in a stage whisper*) I am studying terpsicord!

BOTH. Terpsicord?

WIDOW. Dancing!

(*All do a comic dance and exit.*)

CURTAIN.

SCENE 4

The Garden of ALADDIN'S *Palace.*

A garden, seats R. *and* L., *cushions spread on the ground. Flowers and plants in profusion. Summer-house can be seen, etc. All very bright and gay.*

At the rise of the CURTAIN, *guests are walking about, also three maids-in-waiting.*

CHORUS OF GOSSIPS.

(*At the end of the chorus enter the* WIDOW. *She is hopping on one foot.*)

WIDOW (*sitting on a seat*). Oh, what a relief! These new shoes do pinch.

SING LOH-HI. Good day, Widow Twankey. Hasn't it been a lovely party?

WIDOW. I don't know, my dear, I'm not as good at parties as I used to be. I feel a bit shy at so many strange faces. (*They look surprised.*) Nothing personal, of course.

SING HI. Shy? What do you mean?

WIDOW. I can't get accustomed to all this wealth, and meeting the Emperor so often. It wasn't so bad up at the palace, but now you see I'm a sort of relative, and between ourselves, dear, I'm never quite sure how I ought to behave.

SING TUH. Oh, you mean court etiquette and all that?

WIDOW. That's it, dears. I don't want my Aladdin to be ashamed of his mother. What does one have to do?

SING HI. Why, nothing, really.

WIDOW. Nothing? Just sit about like we're doing here?

SING LOH-HI. Oh, well, of course you mustn't sit in the presence of the Emperor.

WIDOW. Do I have to stand all the time?

SING TUH. No one must sit until the Emperor is seated.

SING HI. Of course not.

(*Enter* LONKA *and* CHORTA.)

LONKA. Widow Twankey, your new mangles, laundry just catch 'em.

CHORTA. Widow Twankey, you come plenty quick.

WIDOW. Aha! This will be a good excuse to get away. Tell Aladdin I've run home, will you, dears. (*She is about to go.*)

SING HI. }
SING TUH. } Oh, but you can't go!

WIDOW (*stopping abruptly*). Can't?

SING LOH-HI. No one is allowed to leave before the Emperor leaves.

WIDOW. You mean that I am obliged to stay?

LONKA }
CHORTA } (*together*). You come laundry plenty quick, catch 'em mangles allylighty!

WIDOW (*running backwards and forwards between them*). There you are, you see, and I can't go before the Emperor does . . . Oh dear, what shall I do . . . You are sure I can't go?

MAIDENS (*all together*). Quite.

SING LOH-HI. Ah, here is the Emperor.

(*Music, and the* EMPEROR *enters top of stage, with the* PRINCESS *and* ALADDIN *and* PEKOE. *All bow.*)

EMPEROR. The gardens are all that you promised, it is very pleasant here. (*To the* PRINCESS.) I expect he will never want to leave them.

PRINCESS. Indeed, he is already wanting to go back to the market place.

ALADDIN. Only because I feel that there is work to be done there. My honeymoon is over. (*He greets the* WIDOW.) Hallo, mother.

EMPEROR. Ah, good day, Widow Twankey.

WIDOW (*hopping, still with shoe in hand*). Good day, Emperor. Won't you sit down ?

EMPEROR. Ah, a good idea.

(*The* WIDOW *beams. She watches as the* EMPEROR *slowly prepares to sit. Just as he is on the point of sitting he changes his mind and rises. She has to do the same.*)

EMPEROR. There is an old friend, I must greet him.

(EMPEROR *crosses to one of the guests, the* WIDOW *hopping after him.*)

WIDOW. Do have a nice sit-down chat, Emperor.

PRINCESS. Do not be too long away, Aladdin.

ALADDIN. Not long, beloved. But you would not want me to spend all my days in idleness, however happy we could be ?

PRINCESS. Indeed, no.

LONKA. Prince Aladdin, plenty new mangles come your mother's laundry.

CHORTA. We no catchy Widow Twankey, mangles no good !

ALADDIN. There, darling, the first call to duty. The new mangles have arrived. You do not mind ? (*To* LONKA *and* CHORTA.) I will come at once.

PRINCESS. I am glad, Aladdin. I know your

mother's heart is set on this new model laundry. Go, I will make excuses to my father, and then I too have my household duties.

(*She goes forward to meet the* EMPEROR, *who crosses to her, always followed by the* WIDOW.)

WIDOW. Won't you sit a little, Emperor?

EMPEROR. I think I must be going.

WIDOW. That's right . . . I mean, of course, you are a busy man, don't let us keep you.

PRINCESS. Father, Aladdin is called away on business.

EMPEROR. Come then, we will make our way through the town together.

(*Music, and the* EMPEROR, *resting his hand on* ALADDIN'S, *exits, followed by* PEKOE *and everybody, except the* PRINCESS *and her maids-in-waiting.*)

PRINCESS. How empty a garden can seem. I wish I was a man and could go out into the world and do brave things.

SING LOH-HI. You have the house to look after.

PRINCESS. Everything is so new, even the flowers appear to grow without care, as if they too were so happy to be here with Aladdin. Bring me my needlework. (SING HI *takes up embroidery.*) No, not that, the strange new needlework the Englishwoman taught me.

(*She takes knitting from* SING LOH-HI. *It is done on two huge needles, and the* PRINCESS *knits slowly, with great difficulty, making a "knitter's face" of deepest concentration.*)

SING HI. Is it so very difficult?

PRINCESS (*brightly*). Oh, no, it is easy really. (*She points to book which* SING TUH *has spread open before her.*) You see, it is all written here—— (*She reads.*) You cast on a hundred and six stitches, work three inches, and every fourth row make one more stitch; this will give you one more stitch than you need for each pattern—— (*Looks up a little blankly.*)

SING LOH-HI (*wishing to be encouraging*). That is very generous of them.

PRINCESS (*reading*). When you have finished ten rows, drop the stitches that you do not want——

SING HI. But how do you know which you do not want?

PRINCESS. Oh, I expect by that time I shall have taken a dislike to some of them. It's pretty, isn't it? (*Pointing.*) That's the one I am making.

SING LOH-HI (*looking over her shoulder, reads*). Warm and cosy!

PRINCESS. Yes, when it's finished it comes out all holes!

(ABANAZAR *is heard outside, calling.*)

ABANAZAR. New lamps for old! New lamps for old!

PRINCESS (*dropping her work*). What is he calling? Listen!

(*The call sounds again.*)

SING LOH-HI. Some madman, I should say.

PRINCESS. I feel kindly even to the mad to-day, I am so happy myself. Go, Loh-Hi, see if he needs for anything.

SING LOH-HI (*who has been looking off stage*). He has a tray of bright new lamps. Do you think he means to give them away for old ones?

PRINCESS. Run, Hi, and bring him here.

(SING HI *exits.*)

SING LOH-HI (*going to the* PRINCESS). Is it wise with Prince Aladdin away?

PRINCESS. I cannot always live at Aladdin's elbow. I shall do as I like sometimes even now.

(SING HI *re-enters with* ABANAZAR, *who is disguised, wearing a large cloak, and carrying a tray of lamps.*)

Come in, old man, and tell us why you cry such strange wares.

ABANAZAR (*disguising his voice*). New lamps for old, lady! New lamps for old!

PRINCESS. But how can it pay you to make such an exchange?

ABANAZAR. In pleasure, lady, in the pleasure that I give to others. My delight will recompense me, (*he chuckles*) nothing else, only my delight.

PRINCESS. He is very kind and generous. I would like to give him something. (*To* ABANAZAR.) My husband has an old lamp, a very old and dirty lamp . . .

SING LOH-HI. Madame, is it yours to part with?

PRINCESS. You forget, Loh-Hi, that I am married now. What is my husband's, is mine. Go and fetch it hither.

(SING LOH-HI *exits.*)

(*To* ABANAZAR.) It is so very old, I hardly like to ask you for a new one.

ABANAZAR. I care not, all the more joy to see a new one in its place.

(SING LOH-HI *returns.*)

Ah, hold it carefully . . .

(*He tries to snatch it as* SING LOH-HI *passes, but she evades him, and hands it to the* PRINCESS.)

PRINCESS. Aladdin always takes care that no one touches it but himself. I wonder if I ought to part with it.

ABANAZAR. It is very dirty, lady . . . (*His hands tremble.*)

PRINCESS. No one could object to a clean one in its place, and yet—no, it is not fair. I cannot make such an exchange.

ABANAZAR (*softly*). New lamps for old, lady! New lamps for old!

PRINCESS. Loh-Hi, perhaps you had better put it back . . . (*Then she catches sight of the bright lamp* ABANAZAR *is polishing, and changes her mind again.*) Yes, I will give it to him. Here, kind old man, I will have the bright new one instead.

(*The* PRINCESS *hands the lamp, the moment* ABANAZAR *touches it the lights change. His manner alters.*)

Oh, what have I done! What has happened?

(*All scream.*)

ABANAZAR. Aha, you shall learn who is master now. (*He rubs the lamp.*)

(ALHIRA *appears, but shrinking and cowering away from him.*)

Slave of the lamp, transport this castle and these maidens to the far desert wilds, where none shall ever find them or set eyes on them again.

(ABANAZAR *can drag the* PRINCESS *off as the* CURTAIN *falls, or if the lighting allows, the stage should be in complete darkness for a few moments while all exit and the flowers are changed. The garden should entirely disappear. See Note on Scenery.*)

(*The crowd run on, followed by the* EMPEROR, *the* GRAND VIZIER *and* PEKOE, *etc.*)

CROWD (*speaking as they run on, and more or less together, with exclamations of horror*). What is it? What has happened? Horror! The palace has disappeared! See, only the desert again! The Emperor comes!

EMPEROR. What is this? A plague has fallen upon us. Is it Aladdin who has spirited my daughter away?

PEKOE. No, no, it was some enemy.

GRAND VIZIER. It was the magician! They say the Princess was seen floating across the sky on a magic carpet.

PEKOE. We shall never see them again!

EMPEROR. Summon Aladdin, bind him in chains. He shall answer to me for this.

GRAND VIZIER. I told you so, Emperor. Even now it may not be too late. My son can marry Aladdin's widow.

EMPEROR. Idiot! I am dishonoured . . . mocked.

(ALADDIN *is dragged on, bound.*)

Ha, 'tis you who have brought this misery upon us.

ALADDIN. It is my enemy who has done this. Great Emperor, release me, I beg, and let me go in pursuit. My life shall be devoted to rescuing the Princess from her deadly peril.

GRAND VIZIER. You have no life, you are as good as dead already.

ALADDIN. Emperor, I beg you, give me but seven days. I swear to bring back the Princess alive, or gladly give my life in forfeit. How could I live without her!

EMPEROR. Well, go, but only seven days of grace, remember. Strike off his bonds. Pray to the gods, all people, that my daughter be restored to me.

(ALADDIN *is freed. He holds out his hands to the crowd, who snarl and turn from him.*)

ALADDIN. How quickly friends turn away when fortune frowns, but love will give me strength, it never fails.

(*During the singing of the chorus* ALADDIN *holds out his hands to each in turn, but they spurn him. The* WIDOW *runs on and he bids her farewell. The chorus threaten him, and drive him out, as the* CURTAIN *falls.*)

Chorus.

You must go and find it,
The palace of your dreams.
Once again restore us
The beauty we have seen.
Seven days we give you,
So hasten on your way,
For if Badroulbadour is lost,
Your life shall forfeit pay.

(*Repeat chorus with menace until business is finished.*)

CURTAIN.

SCENE 5

The Palace in the Desert.

When the CURTAIN *rises, the* PRINCESS *is standing at the window gazing sadly out into the desert, and the three maidens are seated in a group, on a divan. Entrances* R. *and* L. *A shawl must be close at hand.*

TRIO.

Oh, desert wind, oh, desert wind !
Go round about the world to find
Aladdin who has lost us.
The desert wind makes no reply,
The desert wind can only sigh,
I cannot find Aladdin ! I cannot find Aladdin !

(*At the end of the trio the* PRINCESS *sits down and weeps.*)

SING LOH-HI. Do not cry again, Princess, or we shall cry with you.

PRINCESS. Alas, it is now nearly seven days, and no trace of Aladdin. I should have thought my heart would have broken, I have cried so much. But hearts are very difficult to break. One just lives on, growing more wretched every hour. If Aladdin does not save us, Abanazar will force me to be his wife.

SING HI. Even now Aladdin may come.

PRINCESS. To-day I have learned something that makes it almost impossible. Come here, look down there. (*She points out of the window.*) What do you see ?

SING TUH. Only two carpet-sellers, asleep.

PRINCESS. Watch me. (*She leans out and waves the shawl.*) Hi, there ! Hi, awaken !

SING LOH-HI. What does it mean ? They are looking at us, but they take no notice.

SING HI. They are asleep again.

PRINCESS. We are invisible.

ALL. Oh !

PRINCESS. I have suspected it for days. When

Fatima wants to shop, or speak to mortals, she works a spell that makes them able to see us, at all other times we are invisible to mortal eye.

SING LOH-HI. Oh, Princess, do go and coax Fatima to work her charm, then we can talk to these men.

SING HI. They may be able to tell us if they have seen anyone searching.

PRINCESS. Come, then, and pray that Aladdin may pass this way while we are visible. Loh-Hi, keep watch while we are gone.

(*Exit* PRINCESS *and maidens.* SING LOH-HI *remaining.*
SONG : LOH-HI (*optional*).

If the song is not sung, the PRINCESS *will not exit, but clap her hands to summon* FATIMA.)

(*At the end of the song re-enter the* PRINCESS *with maidens and* FATIMA.)

See, Fatima, out there . . . Oh, do make us visible, and let me buy a carpet.

(FATIMA *goes to the window and looks out.*)

FATIMA. There are too many carpets already.

PRINCESS. But it is for Abanazar, a wedding present.

SING LOH-HI. We will tell him how good you are, Fatima.

FATIMA. I shall have to sweep it.

PRINCESS. I will do that, Fatima. I will mend my ways when I am a bride.

FATIMA. Well, I can see no harm that you can come to. Abanazar will be thankful that you have ceased crying for a little while. (*She goes to the window, muttering.*) Zooma, zoom, all zight shall be, zite for you and zite for me. . . . Now let me get back to my cooking. (*She goes across the stage to the exit, grumbling all the time.*) Abanazar does nothing but grumble, grumble . . . ungrateful dog. . . . I've no patience. . . .

(*They wait till she has quite gone and then run to the window. The* PRINCESS *again waves the shawl.*)

PRINCESS. Hi, there, awaken!

ALADDIN (*off stage*). Who calls?

PRINCESS (*clutching* SING LOH-HI). Loh-Hi, did you hear that? Someone spoke! It was Aladdin's voice!

SING LOH-HI. Madame, you dream.

PRINCESS. It was Aladdin.

(*He appears at the window.*)

Oh, Aladdin, you have found us?

ALADDIN. Princess, at last. All these days I have wandered searching, I thought I had lost you for ever. I care for nothing now that you are alive.

(*They embrace as much as the window will allow.*)

SING LOH-HI. Madame, the time is short.

ALADDIN. I must get into the house.

ALL MAIDENS. Impossible!

PRINCESS. Love knows no such word. There must be a way.

ALADDIN. I know. The carpet-sellers are waking, buy a carpet, quickly. I will hide within it. Send and have it brought into the house. Once I am inside, trust me to gain possession of the lamp.

PRINCESS. I will, I will.

(ALADDIN *climbs down out of sight. The* PRINCESS *waves the shawl.*)

Hi, there below, I would buy one of your carpets, that large one, spread it out.

VOICES (*off stage*). Pretty carpet . . . lovely carpet . . . lady buy, velly charming coloured carpet . . . hard for wear. . . .

PRINCESS. Here is money, (*she throws some out*) be off before the wineshops close.

(*The men are heard going off uttering thanks. The three maidens cling together, frightened. The* PRINCESS *claps her hands. Two boys enter.*)

Go below and bring me the carpet that I have bought. Bring it carefully, and see to it that it does not come unrolled. Be off!

(*They exit. She runs to the window.*)

Aladdin, quickly . . . quickly . . . oh, quick.

(*Enter* ABANAZAR, *followed by* FATIMA. *He looks rather disagreeable, and has the lamp attached to his belt.*)

ABANAZAR. The time is nearly up. Is everything ready for my marriage feast? Let it be a rich one. I must say it takes some of the enjoyment out of life having to be invisible so much of the time. I miss Widow Twankey's cooking more than I thought possible.

PRINCESS. Fatima, am I looking especially lovely to-day?

FATIMA. You'll pass.

ABANAZAR. Eh, what? What are you so anxious to look pretty for? That's a new idea, is it not?

FATIMA. She has thought of a nice little gift for you all out of her own head. A carpet. (*She giggles.*)

ABANAZAR. Stop making that noise. The floor is strewn with carpets. (*He peers at the* PRINCESS.) Why aren't you crying?

PRINCESS. Brides ought to be happy, oughtn't they, Abanazar? There is something in my present that you will understand better than anybody.

SING LOH-HI. Oh, be careful!

ABANAZAR. Eh, what?

PRINCESS. Won't you go and smarten up a little, Abanazar? (*To* FATIMA.) He is not very beautiful for a bridegroom, is he?

FATIMA. Come along, I have put some finery for you.

PRINCESS. And we'll have the carpet spread when you return.

(ABANAZAR *prepares to follow* FATIMA *reluctantly. The carpet boys carry in the carpet, in a thick roll.*)

ABANAZAR. Oh, is that the new carpet?

(*The maidens stifle a cry of fear. The boys lay down carpet.* ABANAZAR *goes towards it, and the* PRINCESS *hastily sits on it with a bump.*)

PRINCESS. No, no, go and dress first.

(ABANAZAR *turns to go. At the door he pauses.*)

ABANAZAR. I am beginning to be suspicious of all this happiness. If you are fooling me, beware!

(FATIMA *drags him away, muttering.*)

FATIMA. If you don't come there will be no feast.

(*They exit.*)

SING LOH-HI. Fatima saved us that time.

PRINCESS. Aladdin, am I very heavy?

ALADDIN (*unrolling himself*). You are, rather.

PRINCESS. Have you any plan? Could we take Fatima into our secret?

ALADDIN. No; when Fatima returns, we must gag and bind her.

MAIDENS. Oh!

ALADDIN. I am sorry, but there is no other way. I will put on her dress and take her place. Quick, look out! Here she comes.

(*He stoops down behind the three maidens, who hide him with their skirts. The* PRINCESS *stands apart.*)

PRINCESS. Fatima, come here, my dress is a little out of place. Will you see what is the matter with it?

(FATIMA *examines it.* ALADDIN *pops up to see what she is doing, and is nearly caught.*)

Is Abanazar nearly ready?

FATIMA. He's coming. He won't dress up properly, he just grumbles and swears, he's no sense of what's fitting at all. Well, I can't see anything wrong with your dress.

(*She stoops to pull down the hem.* ALADDIN *has crept out, and taken the shawl, which he now throws over* FATIMA'S *head. She tries to scream. The maidens utter little cries, and they carry* FATIMA *off stage, just as* ABANAZAR *enters. He looks very suspiciously at the* PRINCESS.

He has a fresh hat and looks very ridiculous. The PRINCESS, *to cover her confusion, giggles rather feebly.*)

ABANAZAR. I am glad you like my appearance. There is a charm in rich finery, but this is nothing to what I shall have when my ship comes home.

DUET.

(*At end of the number.*) Where's Fatima ? Where is she ? Is the feast nearly ready ?

(ALADDIN *enters, wearing* FATIMA'S *garments.*)

ALADDIN (*with squeaky voice*). Come along, it's all ready. But first you have to drink your bride's health. (*He has a tray with glasses.*)

ABANAZAR. You are walking rather funnily ? And what is the matter with your voice ?

(*All appear frightened.*)

ALADDIN. The dust from the desert blows in, it has roughened my throat.

ABANAZAR. Oh, well, come along, you can take your veil off for the feast if you like. (*He puts a hand on it.*)

PRINCESS. Aren't you going to drink, Abanazar ?

ABANAZAR. We will drink my health first.

PRINCESS (*spilling some wine*). Oh, dear, now we must have the new carpet spread.

ABANAZAR. Let us go and feast first.

PRINCESS. No, let us spread it now. (*She runs to it.*) Oh, it is heavy. Come, Abanazar, help me.

(ABANAZAR *goes to her and stoops over the carpet.* ALADDIN *springs upon him and they fight, rolling over and over, until* ALADDIN *once more regains the lamp.*)

ALADDIN (*rubbing the lamp*). Once again, Alhira, come to us.

(ALHIRA *appears.*)

Transport us back again to Peking instantly.

(FATIMA *runs in ; she is wearing a loose robe.*)

ABANAZAR. Traitor!

FATIMA. Take me with you.

ALADDIN. You shall come, mother will want help in the new laundry, (*to* ABANAZAR) and as for you——

ALHIRA. Oraculashta has pronounced his doom. For punishment he must go back to earth without his magic powers, and live there until he earn the gratitude of one to whom he has done wrong.

(ABANAZAR *cowers in rage.*)

ALADDIN. Come, then, Alhira. Take us back to Old Peking.

ALHIRA. Spread out the carpet.

(*Music and chorus, during which they take their places on the carpet,* ALHIRA *in front, and* ABANAZAR *catching hold of the corner of it, as if he was just on the point of being left behind, as*

The CURTAIN *falls.*

SCENE 6

The Street in Peking. (*Front Scene.*)

The CURTAIN *rises upon a slow procession of the crowd, going to the expected execution of* ALADDIN. *They sing the chorus and group themselves in little groups of two or three.*

1ST BOY. Any chance of a rescue, do you think?

2ND BOY. Perhaps he will not come back.

WIFE. He will come if he promised. I wish it was anybody but Aladdin who had to die.

SHOPKEEPER. Come on, I should hate to see anybody executed, but I'd like a front seat all the same.

(*The crowd have by this time all gone off, and as soon as the stage is empty, the* GRAND VIZIER *enters, looking worried.*)

GRAND VIZIER. I do hope Aladdin isn't going to be

late, it will upset everything. You can't have an execution properly if the fellow who is to be executed isn't there. Oh, dear, these public functions are a great worry, although I always tell them to leave all the details to me. Others can do the work, I'll do all the details. Some people think it is clever to begin where other people leave off, but I always leave off before they begin!

(SONG—*optional.*)

(*Enter* LONKA *and* CHORTA, *leading* JASMINE. *The mule is very tired and shaky on its legs.*)

Surely I know those legs—yes, it is, it's Jasmine.

LONKA. Very intelligent mule, mister.

CHORTA. Buy the mule—save him from being killed.

GRAND VIZIER. Not I. I have too little money to buy animals, and I never liked that brute.

(*Enter* PEKOE.)

PEKOE. Father, is there any news?

GRAND VIZIER. None; it looks as if Aladdin isn't going to keep his promise.

PEKOE. My Loh-Hi, gone from me for ever!

LONKA. You lost something, buy beautiful mule instead.

CHORTA. Velly good mule—— (*Mule collapses.*) Leetle tired, perhaps. (*Mule snaps at him.*) Velly playful!

PEKOE. I am sorry, but I have no heart to think of any troubles but my own.

GRAND VIZIER. We are in the soup. I don't see why Jasmine should expect to keep out of it.

(PEKOE *and the* GRAND VIZIER *exit.*)

(*Enter the* WIDOW, *crying softly to herself.*)

LONKA. Cheer up, missy.

WIDOW. My Aladdin is to be beheaded to-day, and —oh, there is Jasmine, my darling mule. Let me take him. (*She goes to the mule and pets her.*)

CHORTA. Solly, but he got to be killed, unless you buy him.

WIDOW. I've got nothing but a button and a lucky threepenny-bit. Oh, please keep him for me for a little while, and I will see if I can beg or borrow the money. (*To the mule.*) You shall not die, even if Aladdin and I have to.

(*She exits, sniffing.*)

(*Enter* ABANAZAR.)

ABANAZAR. I feel rather shaken. That brat Aladdin isn't any too good at landing carpets, and I couldn't take over without my magic. I am beginning to like that boy. I wish I hadn't upset things so. Widow Twankey will never take me back, and I do miss her cooking. (JASMINE *gives a little cry.*) No ? Yes. It is—Jasmine. Well, well, well, have you come down in the world too ?

LONKA. Buy a mule, master.

CHORTA. Save him from being killed.

ABANAZAR. Buy a mule ? Do you take me for a fool ? An old, worn-out mule.

(*The mule goes to him and rubs her nose against his arm.*)

LONKA. Good deed to save life of mule.

ABANAZAR (*a little indignant*). Good deed ! I've never done such a thing in my life. (*Mule goes round to the other side and rubs his arm, and curls round him lovingly.*) Well, I don't know . . . Like me to buy you, Jasmine ?

(*The mule indicates " yes."*)

Come on, then. (*He rubs the mule down, making hissing noise in manner of ostler; the mule revives, and then* ABANAZAR *throws a bag of gold to the boys.*)

BOTH. Oh, gold !

ABANAZAR. Oh, any fool can make that. I'm fed up with gold, besides, now that Aladdin is back . . .

LONKA. Aladdin back ?

CHORTA. Come on to the execution——

ABANAZAR. Haven't you heard? There isn't going to be any execution. Aladdin has brought the Princess back.

(*The mule pricks up her ears and dances off.*)

Wait for me, wait for me!

(ABANAZAR *chases after the mule.*)

(*The* WIDOW *rushes on.*)

WIDOW. Have you heard, boys; have you heard the news? Aladdin has come back safe and sound. Where is the mule, where is Jasmine? I can buy her now. Don't tell me she is dead?

LONKA. Me velly solly, man come along and buy him.

CHORTA. With gold. To save her life.

WIDOW. To find that man and prove my gratitude shall be my future task. I'll do his laundry free for life.

(*Music, and chorus enter carrying* ALADDIN *and the* PRINCESS *shoulder high. Some sing chorus and others cheer.*)

ALADDIN (*speaking through the music played softly*). Thanks, good friends, for this kind welcome. In the name of our beloved Badroulbadour I invite you all to the gardens of our palace, where at midnight we will celebrate this day with great rejoicings and a feast of lanterns.

(*All exit, cheering and singing.*)

Scene 7

Aladdin's *Palace in Peking.*

Sing Loh-Hi *and* Pekoe *discovered.*

(Duet—*optional.*)

After duet they exit. If the duet is not sung, this scene will commence here.

The stage is darkened. Enter Alhira *; she dances across the stage and beckons on each couple as they enter, carrying lighted lanterns. Music of selected songs and items from the pantomime is used as each person comes on. The* Emperor, *the chorus and* Lonka *and* Chorta *come first, then the two maids-in-waiting,* Sing Hi *and* Sing Tuh, Gomish, Fatima, *then* Sing Loh-Hi *and* Pekoe, Grand Vizier, *and* Abanazar, Widow Twankey *and* Jasmine, *and lastly the* Princess *and* Aladdin.

They take their places in a large circle round the stage.

(*Note—The lights are full on by now.*)

(*All these lines must be spoken, accenting the beats in the manner of an old-time pantomime.*)

Emperor. Good friends, I shall not *ab*dicate,
For I know you all *agree*,
That *ne*ver any *Emp*eror,
Could Emp as well as *me*.

Pekoe. To gain the favours of the court
I shall not even try,
Love in a hut's enough for me
If married to Loh-Hi.

Sing Loh-Hi. My Pekoe dear is always right,
(*To him*) I think the same as you,
(*To audience*) But that husbands should have money,
That is rather pleasant too.

GRAND VIZIER. 'T seems to me that not the ha'pence,
But the kicks, have come to me,
Yet I've tried to make Grand Viziering,
All that Viziering ought to be.

ABANAZAR. In the annals of Old Peking,
In a legend 'twill be told,
How Abanazar gave up money,
And instead won hearts of gold!

WIDOW. Tho' my chicks no longer need me,
Mum expects some busy times.
Doing Abanazar's washing,

(*The mule gives a little cry.*)

And on bath-nights, Jasimine's.

PRINCESS (*coming forward*). See the moonlight that is spreading,
See—it shines from up above,
May the joy of this fair city
Be reflection of our love.

ALADDIN. Our Pantomime is over,
Nothing shall our spirits damp
If you will grant your kind indulgence
To Aladdin—

ALHIRA. and his lamp!

GRAND FINALE.

(*All dance-step round in grand chain to chorus and continue as* CURTAIN *goes up and down.*)

THE END.

NOTES ON THE MUSIC

The original intention of the author was that the lyrics used in this pantomime should be sung to simple well-known folk-song and nursery-rhyme tunes of each producer's choice. These are the lyrics included in this script.

Special music was added, with some additional lyrics, by Arthur Goullet and Eric Whitcomb for the original production at the Embassy Theatre.

Copies of this special score, containing the new lyrics only, arranged for piano by Eric Whitcomb can be obtained on hire from Samuel French Ltd. The score contains all music necessary for the production of the pantomime with the following exceptions: (1) Incidental music for Widow Twankey's exit (page 31); (2) "With bag and baggage" (page 40, and repeated to end Scene 5 on page 80); (3) "We gossipy-gossip" (pages 48 and 66); (4) Duet, Widow Twankey and Abanazar (page 54); (5) Duet, Aladdin and Princess (page 58); (6) Duet, Princess and Abanazar (page 79).